GENERAL GEORGE WASHINGTON

Painted as a panel by John A. Woodside in 1853, this portrait of George Washington, after the original by John Trumbull, once decorated the hand-pump fire engine of the Washington Engine Company of Philadelphia. It is now in The Historical Collection of the Insurance Company of North America.

The

HISTORICAL COLLECTION

of the

Insurance Company of North America

By

M. J. McCOSKER

Philadelphia, 1945

CONTENTS

INTRODUCTION

IN 1787 the people of the thirteen American colonies looked to their needs. There was need of a safeguard for their newly won political, religious, and economic liberties. There was need of a Federal army and navy to protect the new states from aggression. There was a demand for a monetary system and public credit, as well as for other necessities requiring national legislation. In order to meet these needs, the Federal Convention meeting at Independence Hall in Philadelphia created the Constitution of the United States of America.

In 1792, another meeting that grew from a public need was held in Independence Hall: the need for sound economic protection against losses on land and sea was met at this meeting with the organization of the nation's first stock fire and marine insurance company. Thus, in the nation's own birthplace, the Insurance Company of North America was born.

When the Insurance Company of North America was founded at Independence Hall in 1792, its founders set aside for the future those things which would endure as records of the company's growth. To this nucleus, over the years, many persons generously added item after item of significance in the history of the nation's first stock fire and marine insurance company. These items may be likened to a family's keepsakes since they were contributed by the members of the family and their friends. Today, these family treasures, together with acquisitions from other sources, form The Historical Collection of The Insurance Company of North America.

Since The Historical Collection is largely made up of presentations to North America over many years, its personal value to the Company is enriched by many friendly associations. The Insurance Company of North America is privileged to be custodian of the Collection which today is performing a singular public service.

The Collection consists of material connecting our company's growth with the growth of the nation. It tells of heroic achievements and steady progress within our own fields of endeavor, and it describes, in visual terms, the many aspects of human service which link the story of insurance with the lives of the American people. As such, the Collection has attracted widespread interest in many parts of the nation where colleges, universities, libraries and museums are making use of its material in furthering knowledge of America's march of progress.

There is a good reason why The Historical Collection should afford interest to our generation. Its material is a record of pioneering experience that springs from the vigorous spirit of the American people with their industry and initiative, their belief in freedom of the individual, and their ability to face the future with faith and resolution. Taken as a whole, this material speaks a living language that adds a greater expression to our lives and to our business activities.

Within these pages, one may obtain a general concept of The Historical Collection of the Insurance Company of North America: here are assembled treasures of many forms that recall the vitality, the courage, and the deeds of past generations so that we of the present and future may continue to be inspired with a sense of pride in our own great heritage.

PRESIDENT, *Insurance Company of North America*

THE HISTORICAL COLLECTION

Painting of BLACK WARRIOR, *clipper ship off Hong Kong, hangs in office of Mr. John A. Diemand, president of North America. Built in 1853, this vessel of 1828 tons, later changed her name to* CITY OF MELBOURNE *when she entered service of the Australian Black Ball Line. Flanking this painting are two rare old American whale-oil lamps.*

*"Thrice I suffered shipwreck; a night and a day I
have been in the deep; in journeying often; in
perils of waters; in perils of robbers; in perils
by mine own countrymen; in perils by the heathen."*

ST. PAUL II CORINTHIANS XI. 25

Keeping the Flag Afloat

THE sea is ever a challenge to the adventurous spirit of man. And the struggles of men and their ships against winds and tides, fires and collisions, as well as against the risks of war are celebrated in song and story. In the records of the Insurance Company of North America are written many tense dramas of the sea. There you may read, for example, of the ship *Industry* from Havre, France, buffeted in heavy weather and driven ashore at the mouth of the Delaware in the year 1793. Ten passengers and the crew of a lifeboat were drowned. The North America paid $4,000, the first marine settlement on its books.

As the largest single insurer of ships and cargoes, the Insurance Company of North America played a part of supreme importance in the critical first years of the nation's life. In his "Biography of A Business," Marquis James writes: "*The freedom of the seas was necessary to our life and prosperity and there were dark days and years when it seemed as if that freedom were impossible for us to win or to keep. Its own future at stake on the sea, the interests of the Insurance Company of North America and those of the United States were one. In the long fight the fortunes of the firm on Front Street were tied to those of the United States as a tail to a kite. Every American flag the company helped to keep afloat was a blow for our side in the battle for national existence.*"

11

The Carrying Trade

Even before Congress in 1794 took steps to build the United States Navy in order to protect American commerce on the high seas, the Insurance Company of North America was underwriting risks for the nation's growing ocean-borne trade. During the taut days when privateering was rampant, the carrying trade of the new nation leaned heavily upon North America's protection. All through the growth of sea trade with China and South America, the development of packet line service between Great Britain and the United States, and during the celebrated clipper voyages to California, a large part of the nation's shipping was underwritten by North America.

Through this period of national development, the Insurance Company of North America collection of marine paintings grew in number. These paintings conjure up visions of the old sailing days in American ports: the waterfront and its counting houses; the smells of hemp, and tar and spices; the yards and masts of vessels in the harbor, and great bowsprits lined along the wharves; seamen at work, hoisting the sails and catting the anchor, while they sing,—

> *"How do you know she's a Yankee liner?*
> *Blow, boys, blow!*
> *The Stars and Stripes float out behind her*
> *Blow, my bully boys, blow!"*

These paintings are historical documents as well as canvases of considerable technical ability. They are, in a sense, colorful descriptions of a bygone day when the sea was a challenge to be met with a spread of sails and man's own faith.

The Magic of the Sea

The earliest known marine painters were the Egyptians, whose squaresail craft survive pictorially upon ancient temple walls. In every epoch, the glint of sail against the sea has stimulated the imagination of artists in every maritime nation. This was especially true in the last century, during the "golden age of sail" when artists, particularly in the United States and Great Britain, produced marine paintings of great distinction. It was quite natural that some of the finest canvases depicting sailing vessels in this period should have found their way to the collection of the first American marine insurance company.

The marine paintings in The Historical Collection are notable for their sincerity and beauty. Sky and water, wind and wave, ship and sail—here are the elements of merchant service on the seas in every aspect. The paintings range from graceful and sensitive harbor studies of full rigged vessels to vigorous and dramatic scenes of ships on the high seas. These paintings recall old tales, too. Argonauts and the rush to California in '49, the ocean races from China when crews wagered a large part of their wages on the speed of the clippers, the tedious days of standing by the braces in the doldrums, and the tense hours of "making westings" 'round the Horn. All the romance and adventure that lured men to sail before the mast are inherent in these paintings and, observing them, one recalls Longfellow's lines:

> *". . . the beauty and the mystery of the ships*
> *And the magic of the sea."*

Etchings in Adventure

Inasmuch as books were first printed at a time when exploration and discovery in uncharted parts of the globe were taking place, it is understandable that some of the earliest specimens of the engraver's art treat with ships and the sea.

The art of map-making, known as cartography, gave rise to artistic engraving, too. And among the fine prints in The Historical Collection are rare maps from the days when a large area of the world remained unknown except as coastlines to intrepid voyagers.

Many prints relating to marine adventure, gems of the engraver's skill, also form an interesting complement to the marine paintings in The Historical Collection. For example, there are engravings by Robert Dodd, who gives us accurate examples of sails and rigging of the vessels which ploughed the troublous seas at a time when the Insurance Company of North America was about to be formed. A contemporary of Dodd, was John Boydell, a Shropshire lad born in 1719, whose engraving of the engagement of the "Bon Homme Richard" with the "Serapis" left a brilliant memorial to the seamanship of Captain John Paul Jones.

Represented in The Historical Collection is a print of the "Himalaya," an epochal screw-propelled steamboat. Dated in 1853, this print is from the work of T. G. Dutton whose interpretations of British maritime life from 1845 to 1878 cover the exciting and decisive race for supremacy between sail and steam on the high seas.

On this side of the Atlantic, Thomas Birch painted the U. S. Frigate "United States" in its successful encounter with the British Frigate "Macedonian." This American naval vessel, commanded by Stephen Decatur, was launched only a short walk from the early offices of the Insurance Company of North America, at the first Navy Yard in the United States. An engraving of this painting lends added historical significance to the marine prints in North America's Collection.

MARINE PAINTINGS

1A • WARRIOR, American armed brig, circa 1812, 430 tons. Oil painting by Thomas Birch (1779-1851), showing action between WARRIOR, letter-of-marque brig, and British armed schooner HOPE in 1814. The WARRIOR, under the command of Captain Guy R. Champlin, came upon the HOPE bound from Glasgow to Buenos Aires and took her as a prize. (*Illustrated*).

2A • PEEP O' DAY, British brig. Flies Marryat signal flags for year 1869, together with East India Company flag. Oil painting contemporary with vessel.

3A • BERLIN, American sail ship, built at Phippsburg, Maine by C. V. Minott; 1634 tons. In 1850 when this ship was new, the size of ships had increased considerably. Half century before, the GRAND TURK, of Salem, was considered a very large vessel at 564 tons. Oil painting contemporary with vessel.

4A • BLACK WARRIOR, medium clipper ship. 1828 tons. Built in 1853 by Austin & Co., Damariscotta, Maine. Owned first by Wm. Wilson & Co., of Baltimore, this clipper was sold to the Australian Black Ball Line, and her name changed to the CITY OF MELBOURNE. 234 ft. long, 42 ft. in the beam and 23 ft., 8 inches deep, her dimensions afford an idea of the medium clipper's build. Oil painting contemporary with vessel. (*Illustrated*).

5A • CHAMPLAIN, American ship. Built at New York in 1834. Owned by Wm. Platt, Hugh F. Hollingshead et al., of Philadelphia, this vessel made many voyages to China in the tea trade. 624 tons, 131 ft. long, and 32 ft. in beam, her dimensions make an interesting comparison with the BLACK WARRIOR. Painted in oils by Samuel Walters, British marine artist, (1811-1882). Dated 1837. (*Illustrated*).

6A • JAMES BAINES, extreme clipper, 2515 tons, built by Donald McKay, famed American clipper-builder, at East Boston. On her maiden voyage in 1854, Captain Charles McDonnell brought this crack sailing vessel from Boston to Liverpool in 12 days, 6 hours. This clipper had a top-hatted figurehead likeness of her namesake, James Baines, Liverpool shipping owner, in whose Black Ball line she once made the astounding round run between England and Australia in 133 days. The JAMES BAINES burned at the dock in Liverpool in 1858. Oil painting.

7A • LOST AT SEA. Genre oil painting, marine scene. Painted by Harrington Fitzgerald, Philadelphia artist, (1847-1930). In same vein as THE WRECK, by the same artist, owned by The National Museum, Washington, D. C.

Built in New York in 1834, this Philadelphia-owned ship, the CHAMPLAIN, *624 tons, was painted by noted British artist, Samuel Walters, when he was 26 years old. This vessel was in China tea trade.*

Painting by Thomas Birch (1779-1851), depicts War of 1812 action when the American armed brig WARRIOR, *under Captain Guy R. Champlin, captured the British armed schooner,* HOPE, *bound from Glasgow to Buenos Aires.*

Painting at Hong Kong of the crack clipper ship MANDARIN, *776 tons, built in 1850 by Smith & Dimon, of New York City. Most notable run was in 1855 when she broke record from New York to Melbourne with a 70-day passage.*

8A • MANDARIN, American clipper ship. 776 tons. Built in 1850 by Smith & Dimon, New York City, and owned by Goodhue & Co., of the same city, this vessel was lost on August 9th, 1864 in the China Sea. The MANDARIN, under the command of Captain John W. C. Perit, raced the extreme clipper HURRICANE from New York to San Francisco in bad weather during 1853. The MANDARIN won with a 123 days voyage. Oil painting by unknown Chinese artist, about 1855. *(Illustrated)*.

9A • MARINE. Oil painting by Arthur John Trevor Briscoe, born at Birkenhead, England, 1873.

10A • MARINE. Oil painting by Arthur John Trevor Briscoe, A.R.E., the noted colorist and etcher of marine subjects.

11A • MARINE. Oil painting by Edward Schmidt, German marine artist, (1806-1862). Dated 1840.

12A • MARINE. Oil painting by William Trost Richards, American artist, (1833-1905).

13A • MOSS ROSE, British wooden barque, 801 tons, built in 1863 by Hilyard, St. John, N. B. She was abandoned in 1887. Painting shows vessel off Holyhead, England.

14A • MATILDA WATTENBACH, sailing ship built at Liverpool, England in 1853. Dimensions: 210 ft. long, 35 ft. beam, 20 ft. depth. Sheathed in metal, this ship made many runs between Great Britain and New Zealand in the 1850's. Later, she changed hands and entered the China trade, having been renamed RACE HORSE. Oil painting by Montague Dawson, British artist. *(Illustrated)*

15A • MEN AND BOATS. Marine oil painting. Small sailing craft. French school, 1870.

16A • NEW YORK HARBOR. Oil painting by Arthur John Trevor Briscoe.

17A • NORTH CAROLINA, U. S. Ship-of-line, battery of 74 guns. Launched in 1820 at the Philadelphia

U. S. Ship-of-the-line NORTH CAROLINA. *A rare painting on wood, dated 1820, of naval vessel built in Philadelphia near North America's first office. An early U. S. frigate, possibly the* CONSTITUTION, *is in background.*

Navy Yard. From 1839 to 1866, she was a naval receiving ship. The NORTH CAROLINA, 2663 tons, may be compared in naval status with battleship of the present U.S. Navy. The present U.S.S. NORTH CAROLINA is 35,000 tons. Oil painting on wood. Rare. (*Illustrated*).

18A • ONTARIO, American packet ship. Oil painting, dated 1874, shows vessel off Dover Castle, England. This vessel, like other packets owned by Grinnell, Minturn & Co. conducted regular passenger service between New York and Liverpool. Painted by R. B. Spencer. (*Illustrated*).

19A • MARINE. Oil painting by Arthur Parton, British artist, (1842-1914).

20A • CLIPPER SHIP and BARQUE. This painting depicts two vessels in dirty weather off Cape Horn, southernmost tip of South America. The names of the vessels and artist are unknown. The passage from the Atlantic to Pacific oceans often required many days of buffeting against gales and heavy

seas. Cape Horn was named after Hoorn, Holland, the native town of an early Dutch navigator who explored these waters. (*Illustrated*).

21A • PENNSYLVANIA, steam-powered and sail. Built in 1872 by William Cramp & Sons, Philadelphia, this 600 horse-power vessel made first Atlantic crossing in May, 1873. The PENNSYLVANIA was one of the first four iron trans-Atlantic liners built in the U. S. Her three sister ships were: S. S. OHIO, S. S. ILLINOIS, and S. S. INDIANA. The latter had a tonnage of 3,126, each of the others a tonnage of 3,104. These four American Line sister-ships were each 375 feet long, 43 feet, 8 inches in beam.

22A • INDIANA, steam-powered and sail. Built by William Cramp & Sons in 1872, the INDIANA plied between Liverpool and Philadelphia, as one of the four vessels of the American Line, the only steamship company of the period to carry the U. S. Flag in regular service between Europe and America.

Painting by Montague J. Dawson, noted contemporary British marine painter, of ship MATILDA WATTENBACH. *built in 1853 at Liverpool. This sailing ship was active in trade between Great Britain and New Zealand. Later, in the China trade, her name was changed to* RACE HORSE.

Oil painting signed by R. B. Spencer, shows ONTARIO, *American packet ship, off Dover Castle, England in 1874.*

The keystone on the smoke-stack, emblem of the American Lines, was derived from large Pennsylvania investments in this company. (*Illustrated*).

23A • SHIP, American sail ship, circa 1840, painted and signed by Chinese marine artist, Sunqua. Probably painted about 1840 when vessel was at Whampoa. Paintings by Sunqua are exceedingly rare. The famed Peabody Museum of Salem has a few Sunquas, and a few others are scattered among institutions and individuals. (*Illustrated*).

24A • MARINE. Oil painting by George W. Nicholson, (1832-1911), 19th Century American school.

25A • CHAMPION OF THE SEAS. 3-deck ship, clipper type. A sister ship of the JAMES BAINES, this 2447 ton product of Donald McKay's East Boston yard was launched April 19th, 1854. Noted not for record-breaking but for steadiness and comfort, her saloon cabins, staterooms, and 250 ft. decks were considered exceptionally elegant. In the Australian service, she was decorated with the standard "Black Baller" colors: black outside and white inside. The figurehead of a full-length sailor lent ornamentation to her bow. After 22 years of service, she foundered off Cape Horn.

26A • SHIP, packet vessel. Origin unknown.

27A • WILLIAM PENN, American ship. On rear of this canvas is a document stating that the WILLIAM PENN, 310 tons, was built in Philadelphia in 1797. Her owner then was J. Field. Later, she passed into the ownership of Waln & Company, of Philadelphia. Trailboard and Marryat flags (code book for 1839) indicate vessel is WILLIAM PENN. Canvas appears to have been painted about 1840 when it is possible WILLIAM PENN, having undergone many changes, was still a serviceable vessel.

28A • MARINE. Oil painting entitled, THE OCEAN, by F. J. Waugh, American artist, born 1861.

29A • MARINE. Oil painting entitled THE BOATS, by George Nicholson, American artist, (1832-1911).

30A • OWEN POTTER, British ship, 645 tons. Owned by Potter Brothers, Liverpool, she was in the India trade. Built at Workington, 1850. Following custom, figurehead was probably full-length likeness of namesake. Painting, contemporary with vessel, by James Heard. (*Illustrated*).

The scene is off Cape Horn, passageway from ocean to ocean at tip of South America. Vessel on right is clipper ship. Vessel on left is a barque.

The INDIANA was one of four American Line vessels launched in the 1870's at Philadelphia, — the first iron trans-Atlantic ships built in the United States. Powered by steam, these ships also used sail.

Rare painting of American ship, painted about 1840 by Sunqua, of Lintin, China. Sunqua was one of many Chinese artists who painted tea trade vessels in this period.

Owen Potter, *British ship, 645 tons. Built in 1850, she made frequent runs between Liverpool and India. Painted by James Heard.*

31A • GREAT WESTERN, Trans-Atlantic paddle-wheel steamship. This vessel was the pioneer of the great Atlantic steam liners. Built by Patterson at Bristol, England this wooden vessel was first to be designed with coal enough to steam across the Atlantic Ocean. The engraving is by R. G. and A. W. Rieve, of London, after the painting by Joseph Walter (1783-1856). Dated 1840.

32A • GREAT WESTERN, Trans-Atlantic paddle-wheel steamship. This vessel was registered at 1340 tons. She was 236 ft. long, and her draught was 16 ft., requiring a good channel. Her huge paddle-boxes were 58.4 ft. On her maiden voyage, she crossed the Atlantic in fifteen days, outstripping her sail packet rivals, and burning up 655 tons of coal. Same engraving as above, later impression.

33A • HIMALAYA, screw-propelled steamship. Built by C. J. Mace at Blackwell in 1852, this British vessel was known as "the largest steamship in the world." Its gross tonnage was 3,553, its length 340 ft., its beam 46.2 ft. Built for the Peninsular and Oriental Steam Navigation Company, the HIMA-LAYA never carried the colorful house-flag of the P. & O. as she was chartered by the Admiralty as a British transport in the Crimean War.
The print was published December 1853 by H. J. Buchan, lithographers.

34A • DREADNOUGHT, American clipper ship. Built by Currier & Townsend, Newburyport, Mass. 1413 tons. Owner: Red Cross Line operating between New York and Liverpool. Hull resembled sailing packet but heavy rig and other points serve to classify it as a clipper. Lithograph by N. Currier, 1854, shows the DREADNOUGHT off Sandy Hook, February 23rd, 1854, nineteen days from Liverpool (dedicated to David Ogden, Esq.). Drawing was made by C. H. Parsons, (1821-1910).

35A • THE GREAT OCEAN YACHT RACE. Three Yachts: HENRIETTA, FLEETWING and VESTA four miles east of Sandy Hook Light Ship, December 11th, 1866. Sketched by C. H. Parsons, (1821-1910) one of the artists on the staff of Currier & Ives. Lithograph by Currier & Ives, dated 1867.

36A • BON HOMME RICHARD and SERAPIS. Engraving of action on September 23rd, 1779 when the BON HOMME RICHARD, 42 gun flagship of an American raiding squadron based at L'Orient, France met and engaged the British armed vessel SERAPIS. After intense fire at point-blank range, Captain Pearson, of the SERAPIS, asked if the BON

HOMME RICHARD wanted to call for quarter. The commander of the American vessel, Captain John Paul Jones, replied "We have not yet begun to fight." This reply came at dusk. At 10:20 p.m. the SERAPIS struck her colors. John Boydell (1719-1804), celebrated British engraver, made this print after the original painting by Richard Paton (1717-1791) which is in the Naval Academy Museum, Annapolis, Md. (Illustrated).

37A • THE LADY HOBART. Engraving of "The Situation of His Majesty's Packet THE LADY HOBART." Aquatint engraving dated 1803 by Joseph Jeakes, London engraver, whose best works are dated from 1796 to about 1815. On June 28th, 1803 the LADY HOBART struck an "Island of Ice" 350 miles off Newfoundland. Loading the cutter and jolly boat to the gunwales, most of the passengers and crew managed to survive this iceberg collision which sank their vessel.

38A • UNITED STATES. Engraving of "U. S. Frigate UNITED STATES, Stephen Decatur, Esq., Commander, capturing His Britannic Majesty's Frigate MACEDONIAN, John S. Carden, Commander." Engraving dated 1835 by Samuel Seymour, one-time Philadelphia engraver of naval subjects, after the painting by Thomas Birch (1779-1851) who, born in London, came to Philadelphia as a boy, and, after a visit to the Delaware capes in 1807, was inspired to become a celebrated marine painter. (Illustrated).

39A • CONSTITUTION. Engraving by C. Tiebout (circa 1777-1830) from painting by Thomas Birch, showing capture of His Britannic Majesty's Frigate GUERRIÈRE. After outbreak of hostilities in 1812, the American Frigate CONSTITUTION, under the command of Captain Isaac Hull, sighted the GUERRIÈRE southeast of Halifax in late afternoon. By 6 p.m. the two frigates were at close range. The mizzenmast of the British frigate was felled and the battle ended with the GUERRIÈRE's surrender.

40A • UNITED STATES. Engraving by Samuel Seymour after the painting by Thomas Birch showing the capture of H.B.M. Frigate MACEDONIAN. The UNITED STATES, designed by Philadelphia's Joshua Humphreys, was the first frigate in the U. S. Navy. Launched May 10th, 1797, she carried 44 guns and was entered at 1576 tons. She was built a short distance from the North America's early quarters in Philadelphia.

Boydell's engraving after Paton's painting of 1779 naval fight of a converted East Indiaman, BON HOMME RICHARD, *and* SERAPIS, *with Captain John Paul Jones commanding the 42 gun United States Squadron flagship. American tars, climbing aloft, threw bombs upon* SERAPIS, *which had been escorting a Baltic Sea merchant ship convoy.*

41A • SEA WITCH. Etching by Burnell Poole (1884-1933). The SEA WITCH, clipper ship, 908 tons, 192 feet long, 34 feet beam, spent her ten years of sail breaking more records than any ship of her time. Twice she broke the speed record from Canton to U. S.—once she came home to New York in the amazing time of 74 days, 14 hours—a passage never equalled by any vessel under sail. Launched at New York, December 8th, 1846 from the yard of Smith & Dimon, she was ably commanded by Captain Bob Waterman. Wrecked near Havana, March 28th, 1856.

42A • BANGALORE. Etching by Burnell Poole. British iron clipper of 1699 tons, she is said to have been designed by an American skipper. Above decks she had the appearance of a New England ship, sporting single top gallants and skysail yards. Burnell Poole, artist, studied naval architecture at M. I. T. He was official artist to British Fleet in World War I. His paintings hang in United States Naval Academy.

43A • FLYING CLOUD. Etching by Burnell Poole. American clipper vessel built by Donald McKay in 1851 at East Boston for Grinnell, Minturn & Co. She still holds the sail record, equalled only once, from New York to San Francisco. Her speed under the command of Captain Josiah Perkins Creecy, himself a Down East product, is celebrated in American maritime annals. Her main yard was 82 ft. long, and her main mast 88 ft. long. The FLYING CLOUD ended her days by a fire while at St. John, New Brunswick.

On October 25th, 1812, the 44 gun U. S. Frigate UNITED STATES, *first vessel of its kind in the United States Navy, defeated and captured the British Frigate* MACEDONIAN. *Designed by a Philadelphia Quaker, Joshua Humphreys, the* UNITED STATES *was commanded in this battle by Stephen Decatur. The engraving is by Samuel Seymour, after the painting by Thomas Birch.*

44A • MONITOR AND MERRIMAC. Engraving by William B. P. Closson, signed by the artist, William Formsley Halsall (1841-1919). Engraving limns action at close range between the Confederate MERRIMAC, and the Federal MONITOR,—the celebrated "cheesebox on a raft." Meeting each other in Hampton Roads, off Virginia, a furious battle was fought. Although damage was inflicted by each iron-clad, both survived the fray. The iron-clad and the revolving turret were thus introduced to United States naval armament.

45A-48A • RAMILLIES. His Britannic Majesty's Flagship. A set of four brilliant aquatint impressions by Francis Jukes (1745-1812), showing the RAMILLIES in "A Storm Coming," "The Storm Increases," "The Ramillies Water Logged" (with

Admiral and crew quitting the wreck) and "The Ramillies Destroyed." This is a stirring pictorial drama of the high seas in the year 1782 after the paintings by Robert Dodd (1748-c. 1816). Inscribed "To Rear Admiral Thomas Graves, this set of prints representing the Hurricane that destroyed his Squadron at Sea on the 16th of September 1782 with various situations of His Majesty's Ship RAMILLIES &c. the Prize Ships of War and Convoy."

49A • SABINE. Engraving of the rescue of a battalion of United States Marines from the Federal Transport "Governor" off the coast of South Carolina, 1861.

50A • SHIPWRECK. Engraving depicting foundering of vessel off the coast of Oregon.

Hand-colored engraved map by Van Loon, Amsterdam cartographer, 1699. Cartouche bears representations of Indians in New World. Note that North America terrain in this map indicates a north-west passage to the Pacific by water routes, a theory dearly held by many cartographers, due to Indian legends. Since this map was for French consumption, "New France" occupies vast regions of what is now the U. S. continental span. On this map, California is an island.

51A • JOHN ZITTLOSEN, barque, built at Tusket, N.S. in 1864. Owner was J. C. Merryman, New York City.

52A • MAP. Eastern and Western Hemispheres. Engraving, hand-colored, with decorative borders. Amsterdam, 1700. Frederick De Wit, Dutch cartographer, maker of sea charts and world maps.

53A • MAP. Eastern and Western Hemispheres. Engraving, hand-colored, with decorative cartouche. Amsterdam, 1700.

54A • MAP. Asia. Showing Dutch cartographer's concept of Malay Peninsula and East Indies in 1641, when Dutch, Portuguese, Spanish and British Merchantmen were vying with one another for rich trade routes of the East. Engraving, hand-colored, with cartouche. After Henry Hondius, (1587-1638), a relative of the famed Flemish cartographer, Mercator. The work of Jan Jansson, Amsterdam, 1641.

55A • MAP. North and South America. Engraving, hand-colored, with cartouche. H. Van Loon, Amsterdam, 1699. (*Illustrated*).

56A • SHANNON. His Majesty's Frigate, SHANNON, carrying the U. S. Frigate CHESAPEAKE by boarding in sight of Boston harbor during the War of 1812. On this occasion the American commander, Captain Lawrence, uttered his immortal lines: "Don't give up the ship." Engraving after painting by Thomas Whitcombe, British artist (1783-1834).

...s at Auction, for
...ry Goods.

..., *John Connelly*, Old City Auc-
...No. 78, fouth Front ftreet.
..., *William Shannon*, No. 183,
...ftreet.
...oon, *Hiltzheimer & Co.* No. 73,
...and Second ftreets.
...on, *Edward Fox.*
...oon, *Footman & Co.*
...on, *William Shannon.*
...oon, *John Connelly.*
...oon, *Hiltzheimer & Co.*

...on, *Edward Fox*, No. 56, fouth
...ftreet.
...oon, *Footman & Co.* No. 65, fouth
...ftreet

Auction Room.

...s of fale are as follows, viz.
...ferved for tranfient fales.
...ning at 9 o'clock for houfhold
...c. at the auction room.
...noon at 2 o'clock for dry goods,
...at the auction room.
...orning at 11 o'clock, for horfes,
...e horfe market.
...referved for tranfient fales.
...ng at 9 o'clock, for dry goods,
...at the auction room.
...oon at 2 o'clock, for houfhold
...c. at the auction room.
...rning at 11 o'clock for horfes,
...horfe market.
...s, lands, fhipping, ftock, &c. at
...fee houfe, punctually and thank-
...on any evening his friends may
...im.   oct 24

...f a brick houfe.

...he 19th inft at 7 o'clock in the
...he merchant's coffee houfe,
...be fold by auction,
...ck houfe, two ftory brick kitchen
...fituate on the north fide of Pew-
...near to Second ftreet, and oppo-
...ch) No. 33.
...et front on the alley, and 30 feet
...and rent, and the purchafer can
...hree months.
...all be fhewn by applying at the
...s, one half cafh, the other in fix
...eft and fecurity.
...Wm. SHANNON, auctioneer.

...y the 19th Septem-

...in the evening, will be fold at
...coffee houfe, for approved notes at

The brig BETSEY.
Now lying at James Vanuxem's
...wharf, the fecond above Arch
...ftreet, burthen 109 tons, and car-
...es about 950 barrels, fhe was
...ry, and has been fheathed laft
...nt to fea at a fmall expence.
...o be feen on board, and at the auc-

FOOTMAN & Co. auctioneers.

...la at Auction

For New-York,

The fine new faft failing floop
PATIENCE,
Captain Willis;
Having part of her cargo engaged.
For freight or paffage apply to the
mafter on board, at the Crooked Billet wharf, or
BAILEY & Co.
No. 41, Market, or No. 93, north Third ftreet.
They have alfo received by faid veffel, and for
fale, a quantity of RHODE ISLAND CHEESE of
the firft quality. Alfo, 70 bbls. of herrings, dry
falted.
ept. 16

For fale or charter,

The fhip PRUDENCE,
William Miller, mafter;
A remarkable good veffel, and
fails faft, will carry 2800 barrels
flour, and lately fheathed, fhe can
foon be got ready for a voyage.
For further particulars enquire of
MILLER & MURRAY.
September 12

For fale or charter,

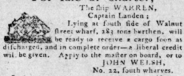

The fhip WARREN,
Captain Landen;
Lying at fouth fide of Walnut
ftreet wharf, 283 tons burthen, will
be ready to receive a cargo foon as
difcharged, and in complete order—a liberal credit
will be given. Apply to the mafter on board, or to
JOHN WELSH,
No. 22, fouth wharves.
Sept. 15   d6t

For Savannah,

The floop REBECCA,
Lewis Monroe mafter;
Will fail in 6 or 8 days, having
moft of the cargo engaged. For
freight or paffage apply on board at
Say's wharf, third above Market ftreet, or to
JOSEPH THOMAS,
No. 59, north Front ftreet.
September 16   d6t

Old Lifbon Wine.

About 40 quarter cafks, landing from on board
the brig Betfey, captain Abbott, from Lifbon, lying
at Moreton's wharf—for fale on reasonable terms.
ALSO FOR SALE,

The faid brig.

Juft as fhe arrived from fea, is in
very good order, having undergone
a very thorough repair before her
laft voyage. Terms of payment will be made eafy.
Apply to
IMLAY & TUTHILL,
No. 89, north Water ftreet.
Sept. 13

For Belfaft,

The brig ABIGAIL,
To fail in ten or twelve days,
having two thirds of her cargo ready
to go on board. For freight or paffage apply to
GAMBLE & HELMUTH.

For Charter,

A good SHIP,
Of 240 tons burthen, will be
ready to receive a cargo in a few
days, and being partly ballafted
would proceed to the Chefapeake
in cafe freight fhould from thence offer. For terms
apply at No. 279, fouth Front ftreet.
Auguft 31

For London,

The ship
FAIR AMERICAN,
To fail in 10 or 12 days, hav-
ing two thirds of her cargo ready
to go on board. For freight of
the remainder apply to
JAMES CAMPBELL, or
WM. & SAM. KEITH.
N. B. Said fhip has excellent accommodations for
paffengers.
September 8

For Charter,

The fhip FARMER,
John M'Collom, mafter;
A new veffel, Philadelphia
built of live oak and cedar,
burthen 230 tons. Apply to
JOHN SAVAGE.
Who has for fale,
A few hhds. and cafes of claret
And a quantity of cotton
Entitled to the drawback
Auguft 13

For Sale,

The fhip STAR,
John Vanneman, mafter;
Lying at Walnut ftreet wharf,
Philadelphia built of live oak
and cedar, will carry about 3200
barrels is two years old, and in complete order to
receive a cargo. For terms apply to
THOMAS & JOHN KETLAND.
Who have alfo for fale faid veffel's cargo,
Confifting of
Wine and porter bottles
Window glafs, 6 by 8, to 16 by 12
Pipes in boxes
Earthenware in crates
Grindftones, coals, whiting, &c. &c.
Auguft 30

For London,

The capital fhip
CERES,
Will fail foon. For freight or
paffage apply to
Meffrs. DAVY, ROBERTS & Co. or to
JOHN VAUGHAN.
September 12

For Alexandria, Georgetown, and Federal City,

The faft failing floop WILLIAM,
Captain White;
To fail in 6 days. For freight or
paffage apply to the captain on board,
at John Waln's wharf, the firft below the Draw-

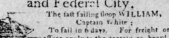

In 1796 Philadelphia was the leading port of the United States. This excerpt from the front page of a newspaper in that year reveals extensive maritime activities. Note advertisement at lower right: Alexandria was a humming port, and, across the Potomac, stood the "Federal City," now Washington.

Watch on Watch

*R*alph Waldo Emerson, sailing in a packet vessel from Boston to England, wrote: "Watchfulness is the law of the ship, watch on watch, for advantage and for life."

Emerson's observation might well apply to the running of a business since, in its long experience with the maritime life of the nation, the Insurance Company of North America kept watch on watch upon ships and their intrepid voyages. Out of this vast and intimate knowledge of maritime and nautical affairs, the North America has preserved a large amount of scarce material relating to the maritime history of the nation. Among its records and in its collected early atlases, charts, surveys, books and newspapers, one finds a wide and comprehensive picture of the "carrying trade" in the days when sea commerce was the nation's life-blood. Here, one finds many items concerning merchant vessels now celebrated in legend and lore.

These are records of heartache and jubilation, of news about ship-wrecks and reports of swift, successful voyages. So important was shipping in early days, many newspapers carried maritime news on their front pages to the exclusion of other news.

Many of the journals and documents in this collection treat with critical times for America during the early 19th Century. These were years of war and peace. And, they were years of growth. During the period between 1805 and 1821, America had fought a successful war, proved its naval power, and added Ohio, Louisiana, Indiana, Mississippi, Illinois, Alabama, Maine and Missouri to its Union.

As records of America's early coastal frontiers, these papers are reflections of the dramatic and exciting epoch when the commerce of the sea was the prime mover of the nation's expansion.

For Bravery on the Waters

On this page a silver tureen with an unusual historical association is reproduced. This handsome example of the silversmith's art was presented by the presidents of a group of early American marine insurance companies, together with a number of individual underwriters, to the master of a British vessel for his heroism in coming to the aid of the distressed Indiaman *Asia*, of Philadelphia.

This tureen, which for years reposed in Glasgow, bears the following inscription:

"*To* PHILIP MAUGHAN, *Commander Honorable East India Company Brigantine Antelope, in testimony of the sense entertained of the manly and important services rendered by him in contributing to the rescue of the American Ship Asia of Philadelphia, Captain Williamson, from imminent peril at the mouth of the Tigris in the month of September 1807.*

This is respectfully presented by

JOHN HILLINS	*Maryland Insurance Company of Baltimore*
SAMUEL STERRETT	*Union Insurance Company of Baltimore*
ALEXANDER MCKIM	*Baltimore Insurance Company*
JOHN INSKEEP	*Insurance Company of North America*
JAMES S. COX	*Insurance Company of the State of Penna.*
SAMUEL W. FISHER	*Philadelphia Insurance Company*
GEORGE LATIMER	*Union Insurance Co. of Philadelphia*
THOMAS FITZSIMONS	*Delaware Insurance Co. of Philadelphia*
DAVID LEWIS	*Phoenix Insurance Co. of Philadelphia*
ISRAEL PLEASANTS	*United States Insurance Company*
JOHN LEAMY	*Marine Insurance Company of Philadelphia*

And a number of individual Underwriters."

The silverware was made by William Burwash and Richard Sibley, who began their silversmithing business in London during 1805.

Journals, documents, and papers appertaining to early American maritime and nautical activities reside on these shelves in the agents' reception room on the twelfth floor of the Company's building at 1600 Arch Street in Philadelphia.

MARINE MEMORABILIA

1B • AMERICAN & COMMERCIAL ADVERTISER. 3 Vol., 1807-1808-1809 Baltimore, Md.

2B • BALTIMORE FEDERAL REPUBLICAN. 1810

3B • BOSTON GAZETTE. 4 Vol., 1807-1811

4B • CHARLESTON COURIER. 4 Vol., 1806-1808

5B • FEDERAL REPUBLICAN. 5 Vol., 1809-1812 Baltimore, Md.

6B • FREEMAN'S JOURNAL AND PHILADELPHIA DAILY ADVERTISER. 5 Vol., 1807-1809

7B • GENERAL CHART OF NEW ENGLAND. By J. F. W. Des Barres, from Surveys by Samuel Holland. Rare. Clement Biddle's copy, dated 1780. 1764

8B • MACKENZIES SURVEY—IRELAND. Vol. 1, 1776

9B • NATIONAL INTELLIGENCE. 1809-1810-1812-1813 Washington, D. C.

10B • NEW YORK GAZETTE. 5 Vol., 1806-1810

11B • NORFOLK GAZETTE. 1806-1807

12B • NORTH AMERICAN. Vol. 1 and 2, 1808 Baltimore, Md.

13B • NOVA SCOTIA (CHART). 1777. By J. F. W. Des Barres. Rare.

14B • PHILADELPHIA GAZETTE. 5 Vol., 1807-1809

15B • TRUE AMERICAN and COMMERCIAL ADVERTISER. 8 Vol., 1806-1811 Philadelphia, Pa.

16B • UNITED STATES GAZETTE. 7 Vol., 1808-1812 Philadelphia, Pa.

17B • WEST INDIES ATLAS. 1788. By Thomas Jefferys, Geographer to the King.

18B • BANNER OF THE CONSTITUTION. 1 Vol. 1830, 2 Vol. 1831, 3 Vol. 1832 Washington, D. C.

19B • AMERICAN SHIP-MASTER'S DAILY ASSISTANT. 1807 Portland, Maine

20B • TUREEN FROM GLASGOW. 1811. The initials "WB" "RS" show that this tureen was handmade by William Burwash and Richard Sibley, who began their business in 1805. The mark of the lion shows this to be English Silver. The mark of the leopard's head crowned shows that the piece was made in London. The letter "q" is a date letter. The King's head is a profile of the then reigning monarch, George III.

U. S. Frigate CONSTITUTION, *launched October 21st, 1797 at Hartt's Yard, Boston.*

A Fleet in Miniature

SINCE man has ventured upon the sea, he has made models of his favorite ships. In Chinese and Egyptian tombs, and in churches of the Middle Ages, scholars have discovered models of sailing craft, proof enough of how highly these miniatures have been regarded in centuries past.

The tradition of making ship models continues. During the last century, when sail was still supreme over steam on the sea, many a skilful seafaring man and many a dexterous landlubber found mutual grounds of enjoyment by spending leisure hours at making models of their favorite vessels. Sometimes this process was reversed: in shipyards, the model was often built before the construction of the vessel itself.

In The Historical Collection of the Insurance Company of North America more than a score of vessel models are represented, most of them made in olden days when the model builder could authenticate rigging and ornamentation from ships at anchor. Here is a rich variety of sea-going, coastal, and river craft, a veritable fleet in miniature form. Halliards and braces have been painstakingly fitted in every detail on these models. One almost expects to see a tiny skipper appear on the quarter deck, so lifelike is each merchantman in the Collection.

Two of the models represent a naval vessel, the history of which dates almost as far back as that of the Insurance Company of North America. These are models of the U. S. Frigate *Constitution*, built at Boston, Massachusetts, under the supervision of George Claghorne from designs by Joshua Humphreys, a Philadelphia Quaker. "Old Ironsides," the nickname of this glorious fighting-craft, was launched in 1797 when the North America was already playing a prominent role in the nation's maritime history.

Pioneers on the Water

Most of the models in The Historical Collection symbolize the days when American trade was pioneering abroad and inland.

For example, there is a model of the *Sovereign of the Seas*, a clipper built by the celebrated Donald McKay. Launched in July, 1852 the *Sovereign of the Seas* was built to outsail the previous McKay built clipper, the *Flying Cloud*. This fast vessel, loaded with nearly 3,000 tons of assorted merchandise, the largest cargo ever cleared from the port of New York, was despatched by her agents, Messrs. Grinnell, Minturn & Co. on August 4th, 1852, arriving at San Francisco. When she arrived, having beaten every vessel that sailed within a month of her, flour at San Francisco was selling at $44. a barrel! Her freight and passage money grossed nearly $100,000 for the voyage.

While the seven seas were racing-courses for American-built clippers, the nation's inland rivers and lakes were bearing commerce for enterprising merchants. Along the Ohio and Mississippi Rivers, handsome steamboats carried passengers and freight. In The Historical Collection, these "Mark Twain days" are recalled by a model of a side-wheeler named for Captain George W. Neare, a former steamboat owner and the founder of an agency of the Insurance Company of North America.

GEO. W. NEARE, *Mississippi and Ohio River steamboat model, named for Cincinnati insurance man and former steamboat master*

Ship S. P. Hitchcock, *2292 tons, built at Bath, Maine in 1883. Model by Capt. Frederick Williamson.*

MARINE MODELS

1C • CHINESE JUNK. Type of craft used in gorges of the Upper Yangtsze River in Hopeh Province, China. Most cargo in this region is carried by junks of this character. River currents are fast in the upper Yangtsze although the water does not permit deep craft. Bristles, goat skins, and other products are carried downstream at right-of-way speed. Master and family live aboard, and cabins frequently include a religious shrine.

2C • CHINESE JUNK. Chinese junks are built with water-tight compartments, the stern is always higher than the prow, crew's quarters are aft. This type has a bluff bow and flat bottom to cope with shallows and sand banks. Tea, camphor and grass cloth are usually carried on this "trader's type" which plies along the coast and at the mouth of the Yangtsze. A coach roof of Canton mats and bamboo laths forms protection for helmsman and crew in bad weather. Equipped with landing stage similar to device used in modern naval invasion barges.

3C • DORA. American schooner, circa 1870. Model contemporary of vessel.

4C • S. P. HITCHCOCK. American merchant ship, 2292 tons, built in 1883 by Chapman & Co., Bath, Maine. Made by Captain Frederick Williamson. (*Illustrated*).

5C • GEO. W. NEARE. Model of side-wheel river steamboat. This river craft was named for Captain George W. Neare, prominent Ohio River business-man and steamboat operator. Rare American model, white, black, and gold. Complete in all details, it represents a colorful era in American history. (*Illustrated*).

Four-masted barque, SUSQUEHANNA, *2628 tons, built by Sewall at Bath, Maine.*

6C • LOCH TORRIDON, British medium clipper. 950 tons. Once held record between Newcastle and Valparaiso. She engaged in a famous race over this ocean route with the WENDUR in 1896, but was defeated by only a few hours.

7C • SOVEREIGN OF THE SEAS. American clipper ship. Model of the McKay-built vessel which carried the house-flag of the Grinnell, Minturn Co., of New York City, after she was launched as "the largest ship afloat" in 1852. Her crew of 105 included 80 able seamen who knew how to cope with her main yard which spread 90 feet from yard arm to yard arm. She was commanded by Captain Lauchlan McKay, brother of her builder. 2420 tons.

8C • SUOMEN JOUTSEN. Model of Finnish steel-rigged ship. Built in 1902 at St. Nazaire, France. 2259 tons.

9C • SUSQUEHANNA. Four-masted barque. 2628 tons. Dimensions: 273 ft. length, 45 ft. beam, 28 ft. depth. Wire rigged. Built in the Sewall Yards, Bath, Maine in 1891. Lost in 1905 on a voyage from New Caledonia. (*Illustrated*).

10C • CONSTITUTION. Large model of U. S. Frigate, known as "Old Ironsides." Designed by Joshua Humphreys, Philadelphia Quaker, the keel of the CONSTITUTION was laid at Edmund Hartt's Yard in Boston. Work continued intermittently, and, after some difficulty, the CONSTITUTION left her ways on October 21st, 1797. Her first armament was imported from England.

11C • CONSTITUTION. Small model of the "Old Ironsides," whose record is memorialized in Oliver Wendell Holmes' poem. This U. S. frigate acquired her nickname on August 16th, 1812 when she met and conquered the British frigate GUER-

Brig.   American merchant vessel, 1860-1875.   Double topsails and elliptical stern.

RIÈRE. On December 29th of the same year she destroyed the frigate JAVA after a fierce three-hour fight which justified her Quaker designer's faith in speed and maneuverability plus fire power. (*Illustrated*).

12C • THOMAS HICKS. Model of British sailing ship. Late 19th Century merchant type, built of wood.

13C • BARQUE. American coastwise merchant sailing type. Circa 1870.

14C • BRIG. American merchant sailing type. Circa 1860-1875. (*Illustrated*).

15C • BARQUE. Four masted. Late 19th Century American merchant sailing vessel.

16C • SHIP. American merchant sailing vessel. Circa 1880.

17C • SHIP. British merchant sailing vessel. Circa 1825-1840. Probably made by merchant seaman of this period. (*Illustrated*).

18C • SHIP. American merchant sailing vessel. Circa 1865.

19C • SHIP-OF-THE-LINE. British "74" naval vessel. Late 18th Century. Figurehead resembles 19th Century H.M.S. WARRIOR. (*Illustrated*).

20C • SHIP. Merchant sailing vessel. Late 19th Century.

21C • GOVERNOR ROBIE. Merchant sailing ship. 1627 tons. New York Registry. Built in yard of William Rogers, Bath, Maine. Dimensions: 228 ft. length, 41 ft. beam, 23 ft. depth. Engaged in China trade. Converted to a coal barge and foundered in 1921 off Highland Light, N. J.

British merchant vessel. Circa 1825-1840. Probably made by merchant seaman in this period.

British naval vessel. Ship-of-the-line. 74 guns. Built in Revolutionary War period.

THE AMERICAN FIREMAN,
Prompt to the Rescue.

A popular Currier & Ives lithograph issued in 1858, showing a rescue scene, was drawn by Louis Maurer, (1832-1932), who was on the staff of the New York print-maker, starting at $12 a week. He was celebrated for his drawings of fire engines and trotting horses.

The Romance of Fire-Fighting

YEAR by year there is an increasing interest in the romance and lore of old volunteer fire-fighting days. The literature upon the subject is growing. With increasing numbers, writers of life and customs of early American days are finding that the bygone volunteer fireman contributed a vital essence to the spirit of the day.

The epic romance of fire insurance is another phase of community life in early America, and, as the wheel of time turns, the part played by insurance in the dramatic story of our national experience assumes greater stature. The literary sky is now bright with tales of bucket brigade days, and many libraries throughout the nation deserve a considerable part of the credit for throwing greater light upon this entire section of history.

From the histories of fire-fighting and fire insurance, one learns that a true democracy exists in the united effort of mankind to fight a common enemy. Fire—out of man's control—is the enemy of man. When a fire occurs in one man's dwelling it becomes the vital concern of his neighbors. This principle, be it fire, flood, or armed aggressor, begets among men the need of united and common action for the defense.

The glorious record of man's fight against fire and the growth of modern fire insurance as a protection against fire is an affirmation of man's ability to reckon with the forces of his environment. The library in The Historical Collection is truly a chronicle of democracy in action.

The Volunteer Companies

In 1736, at the suggestion of Benjamin Franklin, America's first volunteer fire company, the UNION, was formed in Philadelphia. This company limited its membership to thirty men.

In early days, volunteers supplied their own buckets and linen salvage bags. Dinners were held periodically; members who came late were fined one shilling, and absentees were fined four shillings. Volunteers were prominent men in the community.

Historical notes on the early fire companies fill thick books. Here are just a few of the early organizations in the field of fire-fighting in Philadelphia and New York, two cities which pioneered in the volunteer system:

COLUMBIAN HOSE COMPANY (*New York City*). Noted for its members' speed and its "Silver Nine," a silver-plated hose carriage, this company was in existence from 1837 to 1865. The "Silver Nine" was the first engine in New York City to be equipped with bells.

EAGLE ENGINE COMPANY (*New York City*), of Revolutionary War origin, was the first company to keep minutes of meetings. These records begin November, 1791. The Company was located near the "Ferry-Stairs, Fulton Street." During the Great Fire of 1835, it distinguished itself by keeping the flames confined south of Wall Street.

EMPIRE ENGINE COMPANY (*New York City*). Organized in 1840, and known as the "Northern Liberty," because of an engine it had purchased from that section of Philadelphia, this company made volunteer history with its tremendous engine, known as the "Man Killer."

FELLOWSHIP FIRE COMPANY (*Philadelphia*). Founded on January 1st, 1738, this company kept ladders in strategic places throughout the city. It was the second fire company in Philadelphia.

GOOD WILL FIRE COMPANY (*Philadelphia*). Established in 1802, this company was located in an area of rough, muddy roads. Shortly after its formation, it pioneered in the use of horse-drawn engines.

Rare portrait of Benjamin Franklin as a fireman, painted after Franklin's death by C. O. Wright. Dated 1795. Franklin, scientist, civic leader, and statesman, started first volunteer fire company at Philadelphia in 1736.

HARMONY FIRE COMPANY (*Philadelphia*). Originated by Quakers in 1784. The company's first "fire apparatus" consisted of three ladders, and the bags and buckets of each member. John M. Nesbitt, first president of the North America, helped his friends within the Harmony Company to obtain a fire engine from a discontinued company.

HIBERNIA FIRE COMPANY (*Philadelphia*). Organized in 1752, and largely comprised of Irishmen, the members of this company included many soldier-patriots in the Revolutionary War.

HUDSON ENGINE COMPANY (*New York City*). Organized in Revolutionary War Times, this pioneering company was equipped with a goose-neck engine known as "The Hayseed." It was located in Duane Street "opposite Groshon's Brew House."

HUMANE FIRE COMPANY (*Philadelphia*), founded in 1794, once suffered the embarrassment of having its own fire engine house burn. In 1795 it employed a machine built by Philip Mason with 165 feet of woven canvas "hoase."

KING GEORGE THE THIRD FIRE COMPANY (*Philadelphia*), changed its name to Delaware after the Revolutionary War. Organized in 1761, it included among members Christopher Ludwick, "baker-general" for the Continental Army.

NEPTUNE HOSE COMPANY (*Philadelphia*). Two years after its formation in 1805 this company was engaged in a dispute with the *Philadelphia Hose Company* over the right of equipping its hose carriage with a bell. A Mr. Park patented the bell attachment, which was first used by the *Philadelphia Hose.*

NORTHERN LIBERTIES FIRE COMPANY (*Philadelphia*). Founded in 1756, it was among the first companies to use American-made engines. A founding member, Richard Mason, was a noted builder of early hand-pumpers.

PEARL HOSE COMPANY (*New York City*). Located at Chambers and Centre Streets, this company was the first to confine its operations to a specific

Diorama illustrating fire scene at 2nd and Market Streets in Philadelphia in early 19th Century. The Court-House is in the foreground. Steeple belongs to Old Christ Church where George Washington worshipped.

area, except in event of a general alarm; also one of the first to experiment with a steam engine at a fire.

PHILADELPHIA HOSE COMPANY (*Philadelphia*). Established in 1803, this is said to be the world's first hose company. Patrick Lyon, a blacksmith turned engineer, built the first "hoase carriage." Six hundred feet of leather "hoase" were carried.

PROTECTION ENGINE COMPANY (*New York City*). This mid-18th Century Company had its early quarters at the Old Dutch Church in Fulton Street. Its hand-drawn engine was known as "The Honey Bee." Members of this company are said to have introduced the "red shirts" which became universal garb for early volunteer fire-fighters.

43

Original painting by Thomas Sully (1783-1872) for the honor roll of the Fulton Engine Company, No. 21, New York City. This company, organized in 1795, had its early quarters in "Gold Street at the Baptist meeting-house."

SOUTHWARK ENGINE COMPANY (*New York City.*) Founded in 1840, and first located in downtown Manhattan, this company introduced the double-deck "Philadelphia" type engine in New York City.

UNION FIRE COMPANY (*New York City*). Organized in 1792. The first engine owned by this company was nicknamed "Shad-Belly." During a large fire in 1796 at the eastern end of Wall Street, it is said that this engine was thrown into the river to save it, so great were the flames.

1D • AMERICAN FIRE MARKS 1752. By Harrold E. Gillingham, 1914.

2D • BRITISH FIRE MARKS FROM 1860. By Geo. A. Pothergill, 1911.

3D • CHICAGO & THE GREAT CONFLAGRATION. By Colbert & Chambers, 1872.

4D • EARLY FIRE PROTECTION—(Fire Insurance Companies and the Use of Fire Marks). By G. C. Gillespie, 1906.

5D • 50 YEARS OF FIRE FIGHTING IN LONDON. By Jack White, 1931.

6D • FIFTY YEARS OF MONTGOMERY HOSE & STEAM FIRE ENGINE COMPANY NO. 1. By M. Thompson, 1897.

7D • FIRE INSURANCE HOUSE MARKS OF THE UNITED STATES. By G. C. Gillespie & S. H. Walsh, 1915.

8D • FIRE INSURANCE OFFICES & FIRE MARKS IN AUSTRALIA. By A. Chitty, 1925.

9D • FIRE MARINE & INS. OFFICE—FIRE BRIGADES. By Bertram Williams, 1927.

10D • FIRE PROTECTION. By Capt. E. M. Shaw, 1890.

11D • FIRE PROTECTION & FIRE INSURANCE IN THEIR RELATIONS TO POLITICAL ECONOMY. By G. C. Gillespie, 1905.

12D • HIBERNIA ENGINE CO. NO. 1 OF PHILADELPHIA. (Rare) 1859.

13D • HISTORICAL SKETCHES OF PHILA. HOSE CO. (Rare) 1854.

14D • HISTORY OF THE BOSTON FIRE DEPT. 1630 TO 1888. By A. W. Brayley, 1889.

15D • HISTORY OF NEW BEDFORD FIRE DEPT. By Leonard Bolles Ellis, 1890.

16D • HISTORY OF NEW ORLEANS FIRE DEPT. By Thomas O'Connor, Chief Engineer, New O. F. D., 1895.

17D • HISTORY OF NEW YORK FIRE DEPT. By Lowell L. Limpers, 1940.

18D • HISTORY OF ST. LOUIS FIRE DEPT. By Directors of St. Louis Firemen Fund, 1914.

19D • HISTORY OF THE AMERICAN STEAM FIRE ENGINE. By Wm. T. King, 1896.

20D • HISTORY OF WORLD'S GREATEST FIRES. By Geo. C. Hale, 1905.

21D • INTERNATIONAL FIRE EXHIBIT (Official Record). By Edwin O. Sachs, 1903.

22D • LAWS OF NEW YORK FIRE DEPT. 1812-1860. By Board of Councilmen, 1859.

23D • MINUTE BOOK OF PHILA. FIRE CO. VOL. 3. Manuscript (Rare) 1821-1827. Phila.

24D • MINUTE BOOK OF THE SOUTHWARK HOSE COMPANY NO. 9. Manuscript, 1857-1860, Phila.

25D • MINUTE BOOK OF THE SOUTHWARK HOSE COMPANY NO. 9. Manuscript, 1873-1893, Phila.

26D • MINUTE BOOK OF THE SOUTHWARK HOSE COMPANY NO. 9. Manuscript, 1860-1861, Phila.

27D • ORIGINAL CONSTITUTION OF THE ASSISTANCE HOSE COMPANY. Manuscript, 1834, Phila.

28D • ORIGINAL MINUTE BOOK, ASSISTANCE HOSE COMPANY. Manuscript, from 1879, Phila.

29D • OUR FIREMEN—Official History of Brooklyn Fire Dept. (Records of Dept.) 1892.

30D • OUR FIREMEN—History of New York Fire Depts. By Augustine E. Costello, 1887.

31D • REMINISCENCES OF OLD FIRE LADDIES OF NEW YORK, BROOKLYN, & HISTORY OF PAID DEPTS. By J. Frank Kernan, A.M., 1885.

32D • SPECIMENS OF BRITISH FIRE MARKS. By B. Williams, 1927.

33D • STORY OF VOLUNTEER FIRE DEPTS. OF CITY OF NEW YORK. By Geo. W. Sheldon, 1882.

34D • THE HAND BOOK OF MODERN STEAM FIRE ENGINES. By Stephen Roper, 1883.

35D • THE PROVIDENCE FIREMAN. By Capt. Chas. E. White, 1886.

36D • YE OLD FIRE LADDIES. By Herbert Asbury, 1930.

37D • AMERICAN FIRE MARKS. Insurance Company of North America, 1930.

"GOING TO THE FIRE" *is the title of this 1885 painting by R. A. Fox and J. A. Fraser, Jr. Horse-drawn steamers began to appear in the 1870's. By 1900, steamers frequently were pulled by three horses. Fire horses received special training.*

The Big Blazes

FIRE was a danger to the American pioneers, in the Colonial wilderness, and, later, on the prairies in the settling of the West. In the cities, too, the danger of fire has summoned all the resources of man.

The tragic horror of great city fires has, by its impact, shaped the methods and policies for safeguarding against similar outbreaks. New York City's conflagration on the bitterly cold night of December 16th, 1835, when wells and cisterns were frozen, led to the introduction of a new water supply. In 1845, Pittsburgh suffered a fire which brought about the passage of stringent building laws. In 1871, the famous Chicago fire, which left a hundred thousand persons homeless, was followed by an era of rebuilding in that city with an eye upon fire protection.

Other cities have suffered seriously from blazes that were checked only by heroic efforts: St. Louis in 1849 when a water-front fire was followed by an outbreak of cholera, Boston in 1872, Baltimore in 1904, and the four-day fire at San Francisco caused by the earthquake of 1906.

No history of the United States can be written without mention of these and other disastrous fires; moreover, the deeds of self-sacrifice at these holocausts will always be a part of the American saga.

In alleviating the resulting economic dislocation and suffering, the part played by the Insurance Company of North America is historically significant. The prompt and full payment by the North America on its policies is an important chapter in the story of how the citizens affected by these disasters were given timely assistance.

"Burning of the Tombs" is the title of this oil painting, an American primitive type, signed by H. B. Curtis and dated 1842. On November 18th of that year, the New York prison's cupola burned. First at the fire was the "White Ghost," engine of the Lady Washington Company, shown in the foreground.

This story has been told by the eminent writer, Marquis James, in his "Biography of A Business."

In addition to prints bearing upon fires, The Historical Collection contains a number of highly prized fire paintings. In these pictures, the roaring and billowing of flames, the firemen straining at their tasks, and even the excitement and bustle have been concentrated. Out of these pictures are projected the tense moments of American history when fire runs amok—with man on the defensive.

George Washington holding a bucket near the engine of the Friendship Company, organized at Alexandria, Virginia, about 1775. He purchased this machine from Gibbs, of Philadelphia, for use in Virginia.

FIRE PAINTINGS

1E • AMERICAN VOLUNTEER FIRE COMPANY No. 4. 1845. Artist unknown.

2E • BUMBLE BEE HAND-PUMPER FIRE COMPANY, New York. Company was organized in 1762 as Protection Company No. 5. 1840. Artist unknown.

3E • BURNING OF BARNUM'S MUSEUM. July 13, 1865. Artist unknown.

4E • BURNING OF FORT LAFAYETTE. December, 1868. Artist unknown.

5E • BURNING OF THE TOMBS, Center Street, New York. 1842. By H. B. Curtis (*Illustrated*).

6E • ENGINE COMPANY No. 4, New York. 1850.

7E • FIRE SCENE MARKET STREET, Philadelphia. 1868.

8E • FIRE SCENE. 1890.

9E • FISHERY FIRE, Gloucester, Mass. 1865.

10E • GREAT FIRE AT BOSTON, MASS. 1872.

11E • GOING TO THE FIRE. 1885. By R. A. Fox and J. A. Fraser, Jr. (*Illustrated*).

12E • HOSE COMPANY No. 6, Ludlow and Canal St., New York. 1840. By G. M. Ottinger.

13E • LANCASTER, PA. FIRE SCENE. 1887. Artist unknown.

14E • PHILADELPHIA FIRE SCENE, Gathering of Philadelphia Volunteer Fire Department. 1836. By T. R. Smith.

15E • ROLL OF ENGINE COMPANY No. 21. 1850. By Thomas Sully.

16E • THEATRE FIRE, Brooklyn, N. Y., Washington Street Entrance. December 6, 1876. Artist unknown.

17E • VOLUNTEER FIREMEN ASSEMBLING FOR PARADE. Canal & Royal Street, New York, 1872. By Pierson Poincy.

18E • WASHINGTON ENGINE COMPANY No. 1, of Worcester, Mass. as members appeared on Boston Commons August 15, 1858. 1870. By Samuel Adams Hudson.

19E • WASHINGTON HOSE AND STEAM FIRE ENGINE COMPANY. 1860. By R. Sawyer.

20E • WECCACOE ENGINE COMPANY. Miniature of an engine side. 1845. Artist unknown.

21E • WASHINGTON STANDING BESIDE FRIENDSHIP COMPANY ENGINE. Water color painting. No date. Artist unknown. (*Illustrated*).

View of the hallway in North America's head office, twelfth floor at 1600 Arch Street, Philadelphia, where America's most complete collection of early fire marks is open for exhibition to the public.

Early American Fire Marks

*T*HE nation's most complete collection of early American fire marks is one of many features in The Historical Collection of the Insurance Company of North America. Consisting of 117 rare and original specimens, the fire marks are on public exhibition at the North America Museum at the Company's head office, 1600 Arch Street in Philadelphia.

Fire marks, or fire insurance plates as they are also called, had their origin in London after the Great Fire of 1666. Insurance companies formed fire brigades to fight blazes on insured houses. To identify their policy holder, the British Insurance companies issued a leaden plate for attachment upon the façades of houses. When a fire brigade turned up at a fire, it looked for its company's fire mark before starting the work of quelling the fire. If the brigade found another mark, or no mark, the members idly watched the fire, or returned to their quarters. Later, these London brigades, finding that one fire is the concern of all, merged into a single fire-fighting organization.

In America, the fire mark was instituted as soon as the first successful insurance company, the Philadelphia Contributionship, was organized in 1752. Perhaps one of the founders of this company, Benjamin Franklin, with his flair for publicity, realized that fire marks advertised the fact that home-owners of good sense insured their properties. Or, perhaps the fire mark was meant to deter a man's enemies against malicious arson. Whatever the reason, the Philadelphia Contributionship's "Hand-In-Hand," the nation's first fire mark, was issued in 1752; in the Collection is a 1752 fire mark—one of two specimens known to be in existence—together with seventeen other rare and early issues of the "Hand-In-Hand" mark.

There are also seven very rare fire marks from Mutual Assurance Company of Philadelphia, America's second successful fire insurance company, whose leaden tree mark provided the organization with the soubriquet of "The Green Tree." (The Philadelphia Contributionship in Colonial days would not insure houses surrounded by trees, believing that trees attracted lightning. Moreover, trees prevented wooden hand-pumpers from getting close to the fire. The Mutual Assurance insured homes whose yards held trees.) Mutual Assurance and the Philadelphia Contributionship still flourish.

Many other interesting fire marks from early companies are in this collection. These fire marks are a record of the growth of fire insurance in America, having been made up of plates from organizations in eighteen states. Some of the plates in the collection are the only ones of their kind known to be in existence.

Indeed, one of the rarest of the early fire marks happens to be that of the Insurance Company of North America. Before being supplanted by its now famous eagle, a wavy six-pointed star was the symbol on the first fire marks of the Insurance Company of North America, issued in 1794. It was long believed that this fire mark, like the extinct passenger pigeon, had vanished from the face of the earth. Finally, evidence came to light that North America's star mark had been placed on a certain dwelling-house. After a long and intensive search, the fire mark was discovered in the outskirts of Baltimore. And, later, another was discovered in Washington, D. C.

These wavy stars of North America are the only two of their kind ever to be found and, of course, are prized as the rarest of the rare!

FIRE MARKS

NOTE: *Number in parenthesis after company name indicates quantity of plates of each company. Total number in collection 465.*

(1-18)F • PHILADELPHIA CONTRIBUTIONSHIP (61)

1F • Dating back to 1752, the first issued by this company, the oldest fire mark in America. Taken from 46 Almond St. (116 Kenilworth St.), Phila. Only one other specimen is known to exist. During the Revolution, many old fire marks were torn down by British soldiers, who melted the lead into bullets.

2F • The only specimen known of this issue of about 1775. Taken from 124 Cuthbert St., Phila.

3F • Issued 1758. Taken from 102 Arch St., Phila.

4F • About 1759. Taken from 24 Queen St., Phila.

5F • Dates about 1760. Taken from house in Cherry St., near Front St., Phila.

6F • The last issue with large hands. Dates about 1761.

7F • About 1765. Rare. Note that the hands are smaller than those of preceding marks. A similar mark may be seen on Carpenters' Hall, Phila.

8F • Issued 1774. Rare. A similar mark is on the Betsy Ross House, Phila.

9F • Issued about 1776. Rare. Note age of wood.

10F • Issued 1802.

11F • Issued 1805 for Policy No. 3016, covering a building on south side of Coates Alley, Phila.

12F • Issued 1811. Taken from 308 Buttonwood St., Phila. The smallest plaque of the series.

13F • Issued 1816 for Policy No. 3331, covering a house in Church Alley, above Second St., Phila.

14F • Issued 1817.

15F • Issued 1818. From house in Spruce St. at Second, Phila.

16F • Issued 1819.

17F • About 1820. Taken from the Cullen Mansion, Morris above Second St., Phila.

18F • Issued 1857. Apparently the last before the advent of paid fire department. Note iron screws.

19F • INSURANCE COMPANY OF FLORIDA, Jacksonville, Fla. (1)
Issued 1841. Company functioned only a few years.

(20-23)F • INSURANCE COMPANY OF NORTH AMERICA (17)

20F • One of two known specimens of the first fire mark of this company. Issued in 1794, when the company began writing fire insurance as well as marine.

21F • After December 26, 1796, the assured had a choice of this leaden eagle or the six-pointed star. Marks were supplied on the payment of one dollar. This issue very rare.

22F • Copper eagle; adopted just after 1800. Only six specimens are known, one of which is on the Bell House of Moravian Church, Bethlehem, Pa.

23F • Iron eagle issued in 1830. Very rare. Taken from premises on north side of Spruce St., east of Fifth, Phila.

(24-34)F • FIRE ASSOCIATION OF PHILADELPHIA (91)

24F • Issued 1817, the year this company was founded. One of this issue is on Independence Hall.

25F • Issued 1825. Also flat iron type. Rare.

26F • Another flat iron variety issued about 1830.

27F • The last of the flat iron variety and the first with knob in back to allow drainage. Issued 1835.

28F • Issued 1857. Made of lead. One is on Old Swedes' Church, Phila.

29F • Issued about 1859. Brass. Rarest issue of this company, only twelve having been produced.

30F • First of the convex iron type. Issued 1860.

31F • Issued 1863. Iron. Medium convexed. No knob.

32F • Issued 1867. Same as issue of 1863, but with knob for drainage.

33F • Thin iron casting issued 1869. Knob at bottom.

34F • Iron casting issued 1870; the last.

(35-42)F • MUTUAL ASSURANCE COMPANY FOR INSURING HOUSES FROM LOSS BY FIRE, Philadelphia, Pa. (46)

35F • Issued 1784, when this company, popularly known as "The Green Tree," was organized. The leaden tree signified that the company would insure buildings surrounded by trees.

36F • Issued 1797. From Front St. and Fairmount Ave., Phila.

37F • First of the elliptical shields. Issued 1799.

38F • Issued 1803. The last wooden mark of this company.

39F • Issued 1805. The first all-iron type.

40F • Issued 1806. The second iron type. Rare.

41F • Issued 1810. The last of the oval iron type.

42F • Issued 1827. Only thirty-six issued. Rare.

43F • LUMBERMEN'S INSURANCE COMPANY OF PHILADELPHIA (24)
Company founded 1873, when paid fire department was beginning to function.

44F • PHILADELPHIA INSURANCE COMPANY (1)
Issued 1804. Only known mark of this company, which started in 1804 and retired in 1844.

45F • HOPE MUTUAL INSURANCE COMPANY OF PHILA. (1)
Issued 1854. Company founded 1854, retired 1860.

(46-50)F • UNITED FIREMEN'S INSURANCE COMPANY OF PHILA. (53)

46F • Issued 1860. First mark to be screwed to wall.

47F • Issued 1862.

48F • Issued 1865. Smallest mark of this company.

49F • Issued 1868. Four spokes added to wheels.

50F • Issued 1870. Last mark issued by this company.

(51-52)F • EAGLE INSURANCE COMPANY, Cincinnati, Ohio (5)

51F • First mark, issued 1850. Tin. Company organized 1850, reinsured in Commercial of Cincinnati 1894.

52F • Issued about 1855. Cast iron.

(53-55)F • FIRE DEPARTMENT INSURANCE COMPANY OF CINCINNATI, OHIO (8)

53F • Issued about 1837, when company organized. Firemen alone could hold shares. Cast iron.

54F • Issued about 1841.

55F • Issued about 1850. Oval iron casting.

56F • CITY INSURANCE COMPANY, Cincinnati, Ohio (2)
Iron casting issued about 1846. Company existed about five years.

57F • QUEEN CITY INSURANCE COMPANY, Cincinnati, Ohio (2)
Issued 1851. Company existed 1851-1870.

58F • GUARDIAN FIRE AND MARINE INSURANCE COMPANY OF PHILA. (2)
Issued 1867. Rare. Company existed 1867-1871.

59F • UNION INSURANCE COMPANY, Charleston, S. C. (4)
Due to Charleston conflagrations between 1700 and 1900, mark is rare. Company lived 1807-1839.

60F • MUTUAL INSURANCE COMPANY, Charleston, S. C. (2)
Issued about 1798, second year of the company.

61F • PEOPLE'S INSURANCE COMPANY, New Orleans, La. (1)
Issued 1870. Brass. Unique. Company, 1870-1887.

62F • CHARLESTON FIRE INSURANCE COMPANY, Charleston, S. C. (1)
Iron casting. Unique. Company, 1811-1896.

63F • FIRE INSURANCE COMPANY OF NEW ORLEANS, LA. (4)
Issued 1806. Like mark of Fire Assoc. of Phila.

64F • UNITED STATES INSURANCE COMPANY OF BALTIMORE, MD. (3)
Issued 1834. Company, 1833-1845. Taken from old barn between Washington, D. C., and Fairfax, Va.

65F • NEW ORLEANS MUTUAL INSURANCE ASSOCIA-
TION, New Orleans, La. (4)
Brass mark issued 1868, when company started.

66F • MOBILE FIRE DEPARTMENT INSURANCE COM-
PANY, Mobile, Ala. (2)
Iron casting. Rare. Company existed 1866-1879.

(67-70)F • BALTIMORE EQUITABLE SOCIETY, Baltimore, Md. (13)

67F • Issued about 1795, the second mark of the
company. Iron casting on original wooden
plaque. First mark was hand-made tile on wood,
issued when company started, 1794. No specimen known.

68F • Third mark, issued about 1820. Iron
casting.

69F • Fourth mark, issued about 1837. Iron.

70F • Fifth and last mark, issued about 1845.

71F • MUTUAL INSURANCE COMPANY OF WASHINGTON
COUNTY, Hagerstown, Md. (1)
Issued 1847, second year of the company. Rare.

72F • ASSOCIATED FIREMEN'S INSURANCE COMPANY
OF BALTIMORE (4)
Issued 1848. Rare. Company, 1847-1899.

(73-75)F • FIREMEN'S INSURANCE COMPANY OF BAL-
TIMORE, MD. (9)

73F • Issued about 1835, the second of four known
varieties, all cast iron. First not found. Company founded 1825, retired 1904.

74F • Third mark, about 1840. Added spokes.
Rare.

75F • Fourth mark, about 1855. Six spokes. Rare.

76F • FIREMEN'S INSURANCE COMPANY OF THE DIS-
TRICT OF COLUMBIA (4)
Issued about 1838, second year of the company.

77F • HARTFORD COUNTY MUTUAL FIRE INSURANCE
COMPANY (2)
Issued when company was founded in 1831.

78F • CLAY FIRE AND MARINE INSURANCE COMPANY,
Newport, Ky. (1)
Issued 1856, when company organized. Reinsured
1879 in Buffalo German Insurance Company.

79F • ASSOCIATED FIREMEN'S INSURANCE COMPANY
OF PITTSBURGH (2)
Issued about 1851, second year of company. Rare.

80F • PENN FIRE INSURANCE COMPANY OF PITTS-
BURGH, PA. (5)
Issued 1841. Rare. Company existed 1841-1845.

81F • PITTSBURGH NAVIGATION AND FIRE INSURANCE
COMPANY (2)
Issued 1832. Company founded 1832. Reinsured
in the Western Insurance Company in 1845.

82F • FIREMEN'S INSURANCE COMPANY OF PITTS-
BURGH, PA. (3)
Issued year of founding, 1834. Rare. Company
retired after great Pittsburgh fire of 1845.

83F • CITY MUTUAL OF ST. LOUIS, MO. (5)
Issued 1861, when company started. Reinsured
1878.

84F • HOPE MUTUAL OF ST. LOUIS, MO. (11)
Issued first year, 1857. Company reinsured in
National of Connecticut in 1901.

85F • STATE MUTUAL OF ST. LOUIS, MO. (10)
Issued year of founding, 1865. Zinc.

86F • WESTERN MUTUAL FIRE AND MARINE INSUR-
ANCE COMPANY, St. Louis, Mo. (1)
Issued 1857. Rare. Company existed 1857-1874.

87F • NORTH ST. LOUIS (MO.) MUTUAL (3)
Issued 1865, the company's second year. Zinc.

88F • SOUTH ST. LOUIS (MO.) MUTUAL FIRE AND
MARINE INSURANCE COMPANY (2)
Issued 1859. Zinc. Company existed 1859-1878.

89F • ST. LOUIS (MO.) MUTUAL FIRE AND MARINE
INSURANCE COMPANY (4)
Issued about 1851. Zinc. Company existed 1851-
1901.

(90-91)F • LACLEDE MUTUAL INSURANCE COMPANY,
St. Louis, Mo. (6)

90F • Issued 1859, year of founding. Tin. Rare.

91F • Issued 1865. Zinc.

(92-93)F • MOUND CITY MUTUAL FIRE AND MARINE
INSURANCE COMPANY (5)

92F • Issued 1855, year company was founded.
Zinc.

93F • Issued 1870. Zinc. Company reinsured in
Commercial Union in 1891.

94F • FRANKLIN INSURANCE COMPANY, St. Louis, Mo. (5)
Issued 1855. Rare. Zinc. Company existed, 1855-1878.

95F • HOME MUTUAL FIRE AND MARINE INSURANCE COMPANY, St. Louis, Mo. (3)
Issued 1845. Zinc. Company existed 1845-1880.

96F • MISSOURI STATE MUTUAL FIRE AND MARINE INSURANCE COMPANY, St. Louis, Mo. (1)
Issued 1849. Zinc. Company founded 1849. Reinsured in Phoenix Insurance Company of Hartford in 1907.

97F • AMERICAN INSURANCE COMPANY, Chicago, Ill. (1)
Issued 1859, when company started. Tin. Company reinsured in Home Insurance Company in 1883.

98F • PROTECTION MUTUAL FIRE INSURANCE COMPANY, Thomaston, Maine. (1)
Issued 1849, company's second year. Tin. Rare.

99F • UNION FIRE INSURANCE COMPANY, Nashville, Tenn. (4)
Only doubtful specimen. According to old records, issued by this company when founded, 1870.

100F • WASHINGTON MUTUAL INSURANCE COMPANY, Boston, Mass. (1)
Issued 1844, first year of company. Brass. Rare.

101F • KENTON INSURANCE COMPANY, Covington, Ky. (1)
Issued about 1867. Tin. Company reinsured 1891.

102F • KENTUCKY AND LOUISVILLE MUTUAL, Louisville, Ky. (1)
Issued 1840, second year of company. Tin. Unique.

103F • UNITED LIFE, FIRE AND MARINE INSURANCE COMPANY, Covington, Ky. (1)
Company founded 1865. Heavy tin.

104F • MUTUAL ASSURANCE COMPANY OF NEW YORK CITY (1)
Issued 1787, when company was founded. In 1846 company became Knickerbocker Fire Insurance Company. Only other specimen is in the British Museum.

105F • LORILLARD FIRE INSURANCE COMPANY, New York City (1)
Issued 1852. Brass. Unique. Company started 1852. Reinsured in Guardian of England 1883.

106F • HOME INSURANCE COMPANY, New Haven, Conn. (2)
Iron casing. Rare. Company founded 1859. Failed 1871.

107F • MILWAUKEE MECHANICS', Milwaukee, Wis. (1)
Issued 1853, second year of company. Iron. Rare.

108F • NIAGARA DISTRICT MUTUAL FIRE INSURANCE COMPANY, Niagara Falls, N. Y. (3)
Issued 1836. Iron. Rare. Company, 1836-1896.

109F • CHARTER OAK INSURANCE COMPANY, Hartford, Conn. (1)
Issued 1857. Zinc. Company founded 1856. Failed 1871, following the Chicago fire.

110F • CITIZENS' FIRE, MARINE AND LIFE INSURANCE COMPANY, Wheeling, W. Va. (1)
Issued 1856. Iron. Rare. Company, 1856-1877.

111F • LEXINGTON FIRE, LIFE AND MARINE INSURANCE COMPANY, Lexington, Ky. (2)
Issued about 1836. Lead. Company founded 1836.

112F • PROTECTION FIRE INSURANCE COMPANY. Charleston, W. Va. (1)
Issue and founding unknown. Retired 1894.

113F • DUTCHESS COUNTY FIRE, MARINE AND LIFE INSURANCE COMPANY, Poughkeepsie, N. Y. (1)
Issued 1814. Iron. Unique. Company, 1814-1906,

114F • MICHIGAN CENTRAL MUTUAL INSURANCE COMPANY, Kalamazoo, Mich. (1)
Issued about 1865, second year of company. Tin.

115F • CHAMBERSBURG FIRE INSURANCE COMPANY, Chambersburg, Pa. (1)
Iron casting. Company started in 1833, but discontinued within forty years.

116F • PEABODY FIRE AND MARINE INSURANCE COMPANY, Wheeling, W. Va. (1)
Issued 1869. Iron casting. Founded 1869, company reinsured in Phoenix of London 1899.

117F • LEXINGTON FIRE, LIFE AND MARINE INSURANCE COMPANY, Lexington, Ky. (1)
Second mark, issued about 1845. Iron.

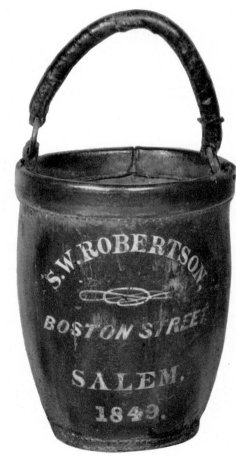

The Water Line Association, formed in 1817, at Lexington, Kentucky, used this riveted leather bucket, reinforced with an iron rim.

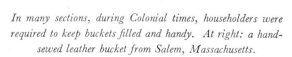

In many sections, during Colonial times, householders were required to keep buckets filled and handy. At right: a hand-sewed leather bucket from Salem, Massachusetts.

The Bucket Brigades

LEATHER buckets formed the first line of defense against fire in the Colonies. New York City, as early as 1686, ordered "every person having two chimneys to his house provide one bucket."

Fire buckets were painted with the names of their owners, and, in Philadelphia, each member of America's first volunteer fire-fighting company, the Union, furnished at his own expense six buckets bearing the name of this pioneering organization.

Householders' buckets occupied a place near the front door where they might easily be thrown to the street upon the outcry of "Fire!" After the blaze was fought, buckets were claimed. Until 1790, in New York City, the City Hall was the point where the buckets were distributed to their rightful owners.

The bucket brigades, in Colonial times, usually consisted of two lines: one line passed the water-filled buckets while the other returned "empties" to the cistern, or source of water supply. It was not unusual in many communities to see women and children take an active part in bucket brigades.

The leather buckets were hand-sewed, and some were elaborately painted with insignia. The fire-fighting companies, of course, owned their own buckets, and frequently employed a squad of four men to carry on their shoulders a pair of poles which held twenty-four buckets. Riveted buckets were introduced about 1820.

In The Historical Collection of the Insurance Company of North America there is ample testimony that the old harness makers and cobblers knew how to make durable buckets. Although marked by use, and more than a century old, the condition of these buckets is excellent.

1G • ACTIVE, C. ENDICOTT. Hand Sewed Leather Bucket. 1830.

2G • A.D.B. Hand Sewed Leather Bucket. 1820.

3G • AMERICAN. Hand Sewed Leather Bucket. 1810.

4G • AMOSKEAG. Hand Sewed Leather Bucket. 1800.

5G • BALDWIN. Hand Sewed Leather Bucket. 1820.

6G • H. HIGBY No. 1. Hand Sewed Leather Bucket. 1800.

7G • BUSTLETON. Hand Sewed Leather Bucket.

8G • DAVID SOWER, NORRISTOWN F.C. Hand Sewed Leather Bucket. 1837.

9G • ESSEX No. 4, NEWARK, N. J. Hand Sewed Leather Bucket. 1810.

10G • "F". Hand Sewed Leather Bucket. 1800.

11G • "F". Riveted Leather Bucket. 1825.

12G • FRANKLIN FIRE CO., GEORGE P. KETTELL. Hand Sewed Leather Bucket. 1830.

13G • FRANKLIN FIRE COMPANY. Hand Sewed Leather Bucket. 1830.

14G • FRANKLIN FIRE COMPANY. Hand Sewed Leather Bucket. 1830.

15G • FRANKLIN FIRE COMPANY OF CHARLESTOWN, MASS. Hand Sewed Leather Bucket. 1830.

16G • FRANKLIN FIRE SOCIETY. Hand Sewed Leather Bucket. 1830.

17G • FRANKLIN FIRE SOCIETY, JAMES BAILEY. Hand Sewed Leather Bucket. 1830.

18G • GETCHELL. Hand Sewed Leather Bucket. 1820.

19G • GETCHELL. Hand Sewed Leather Bucket. 1820.

20G • G. E. ADAMS No. 1, BEDFORD, MASS. Hand Sewed Leather Bucket. 1846.

21G • HANCOCK CO. No. 1. Hand Sewed Leather Bucket. 1800.

22G • HENKLE. Hand Sewed Leather Bucket. 1860.

23G • HIGBY No. 2. Hand Sewed Leather Bucket. 1825.

24G • H.I.L. Riveted Leather Bucket (Red). 1835.

25G • JAMES W. EMERY. Hand Sewed Leather Bucket.

26G • J. BRADIN No. 1. Hand Sewed Leather Bucket. 1820.

27G • JACOB MILLER L.W. Hand Sewed Leather Bucket. 1830.

28G • J.G.W. OF M.F. CO., PASADENA, CAL. Hand Sewed Leather Bucket. 1855.

29G • J.G.W. OF M.F. CO., PASADENA, CAL. Hand Sewed Leather Bucket. 1855.

30G • J. H. CUMMINGS CO. No. 2, PASADENA, CAL. Hand Sewed Leather Bucket. 1841.

31G • J. BICKEL, EAGLE COMPANY. Hand Sewed Leather Bucket. 1835.

32G • J. SCOTT No. 1. Hand Sewed Leather Bucket. 1820.

33G • J. M. PRINCE. Hand Sewed Leather Bucket. 1850.

34G • JONAS WHITE No. 13. Hand Sewed Leather Bucket. 1803.

35G • KENNEDY. Hand Sewed Leather Bucket. 1815.

36G • KIMBALL. Hand Sewed Leather Bucket. 1800.

37G • LAUREL LODGE. Hand Sewed Leather Bucket. 1820.

38G • L. BLAKESLEE No. 2. Hand Sewed Leather Bucket. 1810.

39G • MOODY. Hand Sewed Leather Bucket. 1830.

40G • MARSH CAPON LYONS (BOOK STORE). Hand Sewed Leather Bucket. 1825.

41G • M.H., H.C.L. Hand Sewed Leather Bucket. 1820.

42G • N. BACON No. 12. Hand Sewed Leather Bucket. 1820.

43G • NAUMKEAG No. 60. Hand Sewed Leather Bucket. 1825.

44G • No. 13, JERSEY CITY, N. J. Hand Sewed Leather Bucket. 1830.

45G • N. K. Sargent No. 1. Hand Sewed Leather Bucket. 1841.

46G • No. 5. Hand Sewed Leather Bucket (Red). 1815.

47G • No. 1. Riveted Leather Bucket (Red). 1840.

48G • Phillips. Hand Sewed Leather Bucket.

49G • Royersford, Pa. Hand Sewed Leather Bucket. 1810.

50G • Robert Adams & Co. Hand Sewed Leather Bucket. 1815.

51G • Sun Fire Co. of Baltimore, Md. Hand Sewed Leather Bucket. 1803.

52G • Sandwich, Mass. Hand Sewed Leather Bucket (Red). 1810.

53G • S. Wright, N. H. Hand Sewed Leather Bucket. 1832.

54G • S. H. Hemingway No. 2. Hand Sewed Leather Bucket. 1820.

55G • Solomon Henkel No. 4. Hand Sewed Leather Bucket. 1805.

56G • T. B. Moses No. 4. Hand Sewed Leather Bucket. 1826.

57G • Union Fire Co., A. Stiles, Moorestown, N.J. Hand Sewed Leather Bucket. 1800.

58G • Union Fire Company. Riveted Leather Bucket. 1820.

59G • Water Line Association of Lexington, Ky. Riveted Leather Bucket. 1821. (Illustrated).

60G • Water Line Association of Lexington, Ky. Riveted Leather Bucket. 1821.

61G • Wolle No. 1. Hand Sewed Leather Bucket. 1820.

62G • White Angel. Hand Sewed Leather Bucket. 1770-1790.

63-68G • Hand Sewed Leather Buckets.

69G • Riveted Leather Bucket. 1840.

70G • Riveted Leather Bucket. 1840.

71G • Hand Sewed Leather Bucket. 1847.

72G • Wooden Fire Bucket. 1855.

73G • Wooden Fire Bucket. 1855.

74G to 82G • Riveted Buckets. Various dates.

83G to 148G • Hand Sewed Leather Buckets. Various dates.

149G • S. W. Robertson, Boston Street, Salem, Mass. Hand Sewed Leather Bucket. 1849. (Illustrated).

*Original drawing by Jacob Riegel, Jr. shows Colonial citizens on the quick with fire buckets.
Note fire warden holding his staff and shouting orders.*

Staffs of Authority

COUNTED among the early and extremely rare relics of fire-fighting days in The Historical Collection are fire-wardens' staffs of the 18th Century in America.

The creation of fire wardens in Colonial communities was an effort to protect against fires in addition to quelling outbreaks of fire. In Manhattan, peg-legged Peter Stuyvesant, a year after his arrival in 1647, appointed four prominent townsmen to act as fire wardens. Their duties included the inspection of wooden chimneys in "New Amsterdam," with power to levy three guilders fine upon householders whose chimneys were unswept.

Almost two decades before Stuyvesant's fire wardens, Boston had taken similar steps, and, by 1711, this Massachusetts town created a board of fire wardens, a group of ten leading citizens, to direct operations at fires, to order citizens into the bucket brigade, (levying a fine on those who refused), and to arrest any looters, or troublesome persons.

The Boston fire warden carried a large staff as emblem of his authority. This wooden stick was five feet long with a six-inch brass or wooden spire. It was related to the English Lord Mayor's mace, and the marshal's baton, as a symbol of authority. Indeed, lest the fire warden's authority be questioned, he was required by law to have the stick in his possession when present at a fire. The fire warden's position was considered so eminent that he received no pay, the honor of the position being considered ample reward.

The power granted to the fire wardens was considered a practicable step, and the plan was adopted by many cities. As late as 1817, New Orleans created fire wardens, known as Fire Commissioners, who carried white wands as tokens of authority, "to repair to the place of fire, in order to employ and direct all persons."

Since fire wardens were limited in number even during their period of activity, their staffs of office are scarce today. Highly valued as collector's items, the twenty fire wardens' staffs in The Historical Collection recall the earliest attempts at communal effort in the New World to combat fire losses.

FIRE WARDENS' STAFFS

1H • CORDWAINER. 1750.

2H • FAME, PHILADELPHIA. 1764.

3H • HEART AND HAND. 1743.

4H • STAR. 1740.

5H • SUN. 1750.

6H • UNION. 1740.

7H • No name. 1740.

8H • No name. 1735.

9H • No name. Circa 1735.

10H • Colonial type, no name. Circa 1740.

11H • Colonial type, no name. Circa 1735

12H • Colonial type, no name. Circa 1735

13H • Colonial type, no name. Circa 1735

14H • Colonial type, no name. Circa 1735

15H • Colonial type, no name. Circa 1735

16H • Colonial type, no name. Circa 1735

17H • No name. 1740.

18H • No name. 1740.

19H • No name. 1740.

20H • No name. 1740.

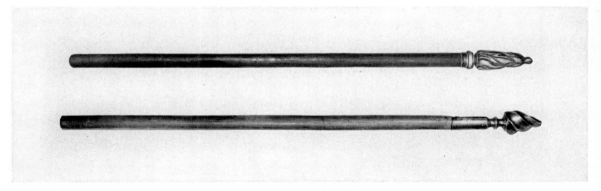

These rare fire wardens' staffs were symbolic of power. Early Boston fire wardens were given emergency powers during a fire: "to order blowing up or pulling downe of houses."

Drawing of the model of a Philadelphia type engine, double-deck, end stroke, which was hand-drawn to fires by the Fairmount Company, comprised mainly of victualers, founded in 1823 at Philadelphia. Note engine side, or removable decorated panel, on the condensing case.

Goose Necks and Man-Killers

THE first practicable fire engines used in America were of British make,—Boston as early as 1678 having "occasion to make use of ye engine lately come from England." In 1730, after a serious conflagration, Philadelphia ordered three engines, one from Anthony Nicholls, a local builder, and two from Edward Newsham, of London: these small engines had no suction, water usually being poured in the machine by means of bucket brigades. Newsham's machines could be operated by feet as well as by hands.

The first distinctively American pattern was the "goose-neck," an engine named from the shape of the pipe that rose from the condensing case. These were operated by side levers, known as "brakes." Until the advent of hose carts, the "goose-necks" carried a reel of hose covered by varnished cloth, or leather.

The "Philadelphia engines" appeared in 1840: these had condensing cases in their centers with the brakes at each end with double rows of men, one row on deck and another on the ground, pumping at the same time.

American mechanical genius asserted itself again and again as refinements were made on various engines. Many machines from Philadelphia makers were introduced in New York, including John Agnew's huge machine which threw water 180 feet horizontally and could be manned by 48 firemen. This machine, known as Southwark No. 38, was the "heroine" of a night when the roof of the Astor House was on fire. She (fire engines, like ships, were always "she") put the fire out at once with two powerful blasts of water through nozzles an inch and an eighth in diameter. Another gigantic New York City machine was called the "Man Killer."

The "Philadelphia," "piano," and "Shanghai" types of engines in the mid-19th Century were usually designed with emphasis on "eye-appeal" as well as engineering skill.   Carved rosewood and mahogany, silver-plated running gear, and ornate decorations lent glamor to these engines.   In The Historical Collection, the evolution of the hand pump fire engine is depicted through unique models of early vintage, made in this country and abroad.

HAND PUMP FIRE ENGINE MODELS

1 I • ACTIVE HAND PUMPER. Hand-carried, early type used in the United States. 1800.

2 I • ATLANTIC NO. 2 HAND PUMPER. Hand-made, hand-drawn. 1800.

3 I • ATLANTIC HAND PUMPER. Hand-made, hand-drawn. 1800.

4 I • BARNICOAT HAND PUMPER. Hand-made, hand-drawn. The Barnicoat Company was a famous Boston, Mass. company. 1830.

5 I • CARSON HAND PUMPER. Hand-made, hand-drawn. 1825.

6 I • CASCO HAND PUMPER. Hand-made, hand-drawn with broad, wooden wheels for use over muddy roads. 1810.

7 I • CATARACT HAND PUMPER. Hand-made, hand-drawn. 1838.

8 I • CHICAGO HAND PUMPER. Hand-made, first hand pumper used in Chicago. 1830.

9 I • COLUMBIA HAND PUMPER. Hand-made, hand-drawn, this model was secured in Columbia, Pa. and was built from a large Pat Lyon hand pumper purchased years ago by Columbia from the Philadelphia Volunteers. 1794.

10 I • COMPANY NO. 2, PORTLAND, MAINE. Hand-made, hand-drawn, crude in design. 1840.

11 I • DARBY RAM. Hand-drawn, hand pump fire engine. Working model. 1830.

12 I • EAGLE HAND PUMPER NO. 3, N. J. Hand-made, hand-drawn, secured in Lexington, Ky. 1810.

13 I • EAST WARD HAND PUMPER, PHILA. Hand-drawn, has solid wooden wheels. Equipped with fire hose, hats, and buckets. 1790.

14 I • ENGLISH HAND PUMPER. Used in Dunstable, England, and presumably constructed by Keeling of Black Friars. Exhibited at the International Fire Exhibition, Earls' Court, London, England. 1570.

15 I • EVERETT HAND PUMPER. Hand-made, hand-drawn. 1835.

16 I • FAIRMOUNT HAND PUMPER, PHILA. Hand-made, hand-drawn. 1823. (*Illustrated*).

17 I • FRANKLIN COMPANY HAND PUMPER. Hand-made, hand-drawn. The engine sides are painted; one side shows Franklin with loaf of bread, the other side shows Franklin assisting at fire. 1810.

18 I • GOLDEN GULCH, CARSON CITY. Hand-made, hand-drawn, sled model, very unique. 1850.

19 I • HAND PUMP FIRE ENGINE. Garden type, so called because it could be used in small areas such as stairways, etc. One of earliest type engines for fighting fire, it was made with wooden screws and hand-wrought nails. 1800.

20 I • HAND PUMP FIRE ENGINE. Hand-made, two wheeled cart with wood hand screw for tipping cart to empty water compartment. 1800.

21 I • HAND PUMP FIRE ENGINE. Hand-made, hand-drawn. The engine sides are replicas of the famous "Columbia Hand Pumper." 1796.

22 I • HAND PUMP FIRE ENGINE NO. 1. Hand-made, hand-carried. 1760.

23 I • HAND PUMP FIRE ENGINE. Hand-made, hand-drawn. Painted red. 1810.

24 I • HAND PUMPER. Hand-made, working model, one of earliest type fire engines in America. 1792.

25 I • HAND PUMPER. This is one of first hand-pumpers used in the United States. Two to four men, according to the distance, carried it to the fire. 1765.

British-made engine with case, full size hand-drawn c. 1720, used by King George III Company, founded at Philadelphia in 1761. This company, comprised of merchants, changed name to Delaware during the Revolutionary War.

26 I • HAND PUMPER, N. Y. Hand-drawn. This model was used by N. Currier in his series of famous lithographs: "The Darktown Fire Brigade." 1850.

27 I • HAND PUMPER. Hand-made, early type, model is original throughout, with exception of wheels that were repaired. 1792.

28 I • HAND PUMPER. Hand-made, painting of George Washington on engine side. 1820.

29 I • HAND PUMPER. Hand-made with foot tread. Pennsylvania Dutch style of pumper. 1820.

30 I • HAND PUMPER. Hand-drawn, two wheels, conically shaped. Used in foreign countries in 16th century. Capable of throwing water to a considerable height.

31 I • HAND-IN-HAND HAND PUMPER. Hand-made, hand-drawn. 1776.

32 I • HAND-IN-HAND ENGINE COMPANY OF PHILA. Hand-made, hand-drawn. 1776.

33 I • HIBERNIA HAND PUMPER. Hand-made, hand-drawn. 1780.

34 I • HOPE FIRE COMPANY OF MANHEIM. Hand-made, hand-drawn, Pennsylvania Dutch type, it is rotary in mechanism. The original is still in Manheim, Pa. 1812.

35 I • HOPE HAND PUMPER. Horse-drawn, cart style, two-wheeler in use in the Pennsylvania Dutch Country. 1776.

36 I • HOPE HAND PUMPER. Hand-drawn, name and motto "Hope—We Save" marked on engine. 1800.

The full-size fire pumper shown here is the work of Richard Mason, pioneer Pennsylvania fire engine builder, who introduced end-levers on pumpers. In 1792, the date on this machine, Mason completed his 117th of this engine type. He was active from 1761 to 1801.

37 I • Howard No. 34 of New York. Hand-drawn, gooseneck engine of earliest type. Secured from Fire Chief of Union Hill, N. J. 1830.

38 I • Independence Hand Pumper. Hand-made, hand-drawn. 1820.

39 I • Jackson Fire Company, Phila. Hand-made. Name and date of company appear on model, "Jackson Volunteer Fire Company of Philadelphia. —Founded 1828." This type was in use from 1828 to 1858.

40 I • John E. Chase No. 4. Hand-made, hand-drawn. Company motto appears on engine "Our Duty is our Delight." 1845.

41 I • Lafayette Hand Pumper. Hand-made, hand-drawn. Picture of Lafayette on side. 1833.

42 I • Lincoln Hand Pumper. Picture of Lincoln on side-panel of model. 1863.

43 I • Manheim Hand Pumper. Hand-made, hand-drawn. 1832.

44 I • MAZEPPA No. 48, NEW YORK CITY. Hand-made, hand-drawn. 1820.

45 I • MORAVIAN HAND PUMPER. Hand-made, hand-carried to fire, used in Pennsylvania Dutch territory. 1760.

46 I • NEPTUNE HAND PUMPER. Hand-made, hand-drawn, early working model, painted side panels. 1840.

47 I • NEW YORK CITY HAND PUMPER. Imported from London, England. First hand pumper used in New York City. 1730.

48 I • NIAGARA No. 3. Hand-made, hand-drawn, typical New England pumper. 1820.

49 I • NORTHERN LIBERTIES. Hand-drawn pumper of Northern Liberties Co. of Philadelphia. Sides painted by John A. Woodside. 1830.

50 I • NORTH WARD, PHILA. Hand-made, hand-drawn with disc wheels. 1790.

51 I • NUTMEG HAND PUMPER. Hand-made, hand-drawn. Connecticut. 1840.

52 I • PASSAIC No. 1 HAND PUMPER. Hand-made, hand-drawn. 1870.

53 I • PAT LYON HAND PUMPER, PHILA. Hand-made, hand-drawn. 1802. Made by one of Philadelphia's most celebrated engine builders, Patrick Lyon.

54 I • PHOENIX FIRE COMPANY No. 11. Hand-made, hand-drawn. One of very early engines. Painted engine sides of battle scene. 1790.

55 I • ROVER HAND PUMPER. Hand-drawn, sled type used in mountainous sections of far west. 1850.

56 I • SALEM, MASS. COMBINATION HAND PUMPER AND HOSE REEL. Hand-drawn. Village type, crane-neck pumper, very primitive with hose reel attached. 1790.

57 I • TIGER No. 6, DIRIGIO HAND. Hand-drawn pumper of Newburyport, Mass. 1840.

58 I • TIGER HAND PUMPER. Hand-made, hand-drawn. The original was built by Bulton Mfg. Co. in 1854.

59 I • UNION FIRE CO., Lancaster, Pa. Hand-made, hand-drawn. 1765.

60 I • WATERVILLE HAND PUMPER. Hand-made, hand-drawn. 1825.

61 I • WATER WITCH, PORTLAND, MAINE. Hand-drawn. 1835.

62 I • WHITE ANGEL, HAND PUMPER. Hand-drawn hand pumper. Providence, R. I. 1815.

63 I • WHITE ANGEL, HAND PUMPER, NORTH SALEM, MASS. Hand-made, hand-drawn. One of best known pieces of fire apparatus in New England, the original is still in working condition and is owned by Volunteer Firemen's Assn. of Salem, Mass.

64 I • ALERT HAND PUMPER. Hand-made, hand-drawn, built and used in Salem, Mass. 1740.

65 I • CHINESE HAND PUMPER. Antiquated design. Still in use in small villages and private estates in China. Capable of throwing a stream of water to a considerable height.

66 I • CHRISTIANA FIRE COMPANY. Hand-drawn, made for the Christiana Fire Company of Lancaster, Pa. 1852.

67 I • HAND-IN-HAND VOLUNTEER FIRE COMPANY. One of the first double-deck engines in Philadelphia, it was considered a top-notch engine in the 1840's. Motto on engine reads "United we stand, Divided we Fall." This engine was purchased to celebrate the 100th anniversary of the Company. 1842.

68 I • J. J. GRAY No. 1. Hand-drawn, hand pumper. 1820.

69 I • KING GEORGE III VOLUNTEER FIRE COMPANY OF PHILADELPHIA (later known as Delaware Fire Company). Hand-drawn, built in England in 1720, bought by King George III Volunteer Fire Company in 1761. (Illustrated).

70 I • RICHARD MASON HAND PUMPER. Hand-drawn, with solid wooden wheels. 1792. (Illustrated).

71 I • VETERAN HAND PUMPER. Hand-drawn. 1838.

Firemen, at parades and exhibitions of skill, wore dress regalia including fancy leather belts, often bearing company names. This group, entitled "Pennsylvania Firemen," was painted on copper in 1840. Artist unknown.

Roll Call in Leather

*T*HERE is an inherent symbolism of duty and authority in uniform belts, witness the belts worn traditionally by military men. The fire fighters of yesteryear, though their calling was voluntary, were mindful of their position in community life. And, although rivalry between companies often led to outbursts of volatile spirit, the discipline as a whole was maintained firmly within each fire company by well-defined rules of conduct. The fireman might be compared to the soldier in his adherence to duty, his traditions, and his *esprit de corps*. Fighting fires—then as today—meant organized team-work, the result of diligent training.

The fireman identified himself at fires by distinctive articles of dress. A hat, a cape, "gallowses"—as suspenders were dubbed—even a simple arm badge were among the early distinguishing items of fire-fighting apparel; these were worn separately, or in combination.

Black leather belts were common after 1800. Indubitably, these were useful for carrying axes, spanners, and other handy implements. Belts became increasingly ornamental as the fireman's uniform evolved into more elaborate attire. In 1850, the New York firemen frequently wore red shirts and patent leather belts. And as parade dress assumed elegant effects, the traditional belts were colorfully designed with contrasting letters of cameo sharpness to identify the wearer's rank, or his company membership.

A large roster of companies, most of them celebrated in the fire annals of the last century, is represented in the firemen's belts of The Historical Collection. In all styles and colors, they constitute a long roll-call of bygone companies in volunteer days.

FIREMEN'S BELTS

1J • AMERICAN. 1864.

2J-4J • AMERICAN HOSE COMPANY. 1828.

5J-6J • ARCTIC.

7J • ASSISTANT. 1789.

8J • 1ST ASSISTANT.

9J • ASSISTANT CHIEF ENGINEER.

10J • ASSISTANT CHIEF ENGINEER NO. 1.

11J • ASSISTANT ENGINEER. 1800.

12J • ASSISTANT ENGINEER, PATERSON, N. J. 1811.

13J-14J • ASSISTANT ENGINEER. 1789.

15J • ASSISTANT ENGINEER. 1815.

16J • ASSISTANT ENGINEER NO. 3.

17J • 2ND ASSISTANT ENGINEER.

18J • ASSISTANT FOREMAN NO. 2.

19J • ASSISTANT FOREMAN.

20J • ATLANTIC NO. 2, LAWRENCE, MASS.

21J • BRADFORD.

22J • BRISTOL.

23J-25J • CATARACT. 1838.

26J-27J • CATARACT NO. 2. 1838.

28J • CALIFORNIA COMPANY NO. 4.

29J • C. F. CO. 1800.

30J • CHIEF.

31J • CHIEF.

32J-37J • CHIEF ENGINEER. 1790.

38J • CHARLESTOWN.

39J • CHAMBER HOSE COMPANY, PHILADELPHIA, PA. 1803.

40J • CHIEF P.P.F.D., PATERSON, N. J.

41J • COLUMBIA. 1806.

42J • COLUMBIA NO. 4. 1806.

43J • COLUMBIA HOSE NO. 4. 1806.

44J • COLUMBIA HOSE NO. 5. 1806.

45J • COLWYN. 1894.

46J • CITIZEN. 1836.

47J • C. V. HOSE COMPANY.

48J-50J • DELAWARE. 1790.

51J • DELUGE FIRE CO., PORTLAND.

52J-53J • DILIGENT HOSE. 1820.

54J-57J • E. A. STRAW COMPANY NO. 1 CALIFORNIA

58J • EMPIRE.

59J • ENGINEER.

60J • ENTERPRISE NO. 1. 1825.

61J-65J • EXCELSIOR. 1853.

66J • EXEMPT.

67J • FAIRMOUNT FIRE COMPANY. 1823.

68J • FIRST ASSISTANT FOREMAN.

69J • FIRE DEPT. CITY OF NEW YORK.

70J • FRANKLIN FIRE COMPANY. 1819.

71J-72J • FRIENDSHIP FIRE COMPANY. 1796.

73J • GEORGE CLAY.

74J • GERMANTOWN HOSE. 1848.

75J • GOOD INTENT. 1830.

76J • GOOD WILL FIRE COMPANY. 1802.

77J-79J • GOOD WILL HOSE CO. 1813.

80J-82J • HAND-IN-HAND. 1742.

83J • HANLEY. 1874.

84J • HARMONY FIRE. 1784.

85J • HARMONY NO. 49. 1784.

86J • HARMONY NO. 6. 1784.

87J • HARMONY. 1849.

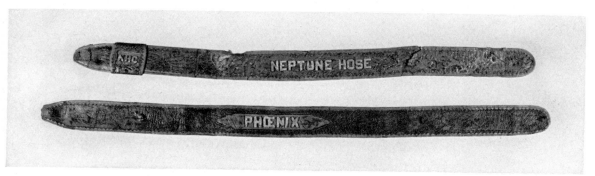

A rare old belt of the Neptune Hose Company, founded at Philadelphia in 1805. The members of this company, priding themselves on their attire, once wore hats showing Neptune drawn in a car by two sea-horses. Also, a leather belt, worn by a member of a pioneering hook and ladder company, Phoenix, of New York City, established in 1805. This company once had a bear as a mascot.

88J • HENDERSON.

89J-91J • HOPE HOSE COMPANY. 1805.

92J • HOSE COMPANY No. 29.

93J • HUMANE HOSE CO. 1805.

94J-97J • INDEPENDENCE HOSE CO. 1831.

98J • JOSHUA P.C.

99J • JUNIOR No. 2. 1818.

100J • KEYSTONE HOOK AND LADDER COMPANY. 1852.

101J • KEYSTONE HOOK AND LADDER COMPANY. 1852.

102J • KITTATINNY HOSE COMPANY.

103J-104J • LAFAYETTE HOSE COMPANY. 1833.

105J-108J • LIBERTY FIRE COMPANY. 1841.

109J • MCLEAN.

110J • METHUEN F.D.

111J-112J • MILTON C. V. HOSE.

113J-114J • MITCHELL FIRE COMPANY.

115J • MOUNT CARMEL.

116J • MOYAMENSING HOSE. 1837.

117J • NORTHERN LIBERTIES. 1828.

118J-119J • NIAGARA No. 15. 1827.

120J • NEWBURY HOSE.

121J-122J • NEW ENGLAND HOSEMAN.

123J • NEPTUNE HOSE COMPANY. 1805 (*Illustrated*).

124J • NEPTUNE HOSE COMPANY No. 2. 1805.

125J • NORRISTOWN.

126J • NOZZLEMAN.

127J • PACIFIC.

128J • PASSAIC.

129J • PASSAIC No. 1.

130J • PATERSON, N. J.

131J • PATERSON No. 9.

132J • PERSEVERANCE HOSE. 1805.

133J • PHILADELPHIA HOSE. 1803.

134J • PHILADELPHIA FIRE COMPANY. 1799.

135J • PLUGMAN.

136J-137J • PHOENIX HOOK AND LADDER COMPANY. 1805. (*Illustrated*).

138J • PRESIDENT.

139J • PROTECTION, LYNN, MASS.

140J • PROTECTION No. 5, LYNN, MASS.

141J • PROTECTION No. 5.

142J • RAINBOW.

Leather belt worn by firemen of Washington Hose Company, of New York City. Once, in a parade of 6,000 firemen, this company caused a sensation by displaying a calcium light—then a scientific curiosity.

143J • RAINBOW READING, PA. 1807.

144J-145J • READY FOR DUTY.

146J • READING NO. 1.

147J • RELIANCE HOSE COMPANY. 1786.

148J-149J • RESCUE. 1853.

150J • RESCUE NO. 3. 1853.

151J • RESOLUTION HOSE. 1804.

152J • RESOLUTION HOSE. 1804.

153J • SHAWNEE HOSE.

154J • SHIFFLER FIRE CO. 1856.

155J • SHIFFLER FIRE COMPANY OF LANCASTER. 1856.

156J • SHIFFLER HOSE NO. 32. 1846.

157J • SOUTH PENN HOSE COMPANY. 1864.

158J • SOUTHWARK HOSE. 1806.

159J • STAR OF LIBERTY. 1840.

160J • SUN FIRE COMPANY NO. 1, PHILADELPHIA. 1778.

161J • SUN FIRE COMPANY, PHILADELPHIA. 1778.

162J • SYRACUSE HOSE COMPANY, N. Y.

163J • TAYLOR HOSE NO. 35.

164J • T. H. COMPANY.

165J-166J • TIVOLI HOSE COMPANY. 1855.

167J-170J • UNION FIRE COMPANY. 1790.

171J-180J • VETERAN.

181J • VETERAN'S FIRE ASSOCIATION, CAMDEN, N. J.

182J • VETERAN NO. 5.

183J • VICE PRESIDENT.

184J • VIGILANT HOSE COMPANY, PHILADELPHIA. 1790.

185J • VOLUNTEER FIRE COMPANY.

186J-189J • WASHINGTON HOSE COMPANY. NEW YORK CITY. 1837. (*Illustrated*).

190J • WASHINGTON COMPANY. 1811.

191J • WASHINGTON FIRE COMPANY. 1796.

192J • WAYNESBORO.

193J • WAYNESBORO NO. 2.

194J-195J • WESTERN ENGINE COMPANY. 1840.

196J • WEST PHILADELPHIA HOSE. 1818.

197J • WILLIAM PENN NO. 4. 1830.

198J-199J • WILLIAM PENN FIRE COMPANY. 1838.

200J • WILLIAM PENN HOSE COMPANY. 1830.

201J to 236J • Unidentified.

J. Riegel, Jr.

Carriage model of Fame Hose Company in Philadelphia, founded 1818, reveals the high degree of ornamentation achieved by the four-wheel, spring-supported, cylinder-type of hose reel. These were pulled in parades, while "crabs," homely hose reels, went to fires.

"Jumpers and Spiders"

A NEED for the management of hose at fires led to the organization of the Philadelphia Hose Company late in 1803. Pioneering in this field, the group of young men who established this company went into action for the first time on March 3rd, 1804 when Israel Israel's stables in Whalebone Alley were consumed by flames. Their apparatus was an oblong box on wheels, costing 98 dollars, and bearing lanterns with candles.

New York City claims to have sponsored the first hose carriage consisting of a reel placed on an axle between two cart-wheels. This forerunner of latter-day hose reels was devised by David J. Hubbs and was known as "Hubbs' Baby." The first hose company in New York City, the Eagle, was organized in 1812.

The importance of "hoase" at fires was quickly recognized as growing communities outstripped available water supplies. In 1825, Josiah Quincy, Mayor of Boston and a "modernizer" of that city's fire-fighting system, pointed out that "every hundred feet of hose is as effectual as the presence of sixty men with buckets."

The hose reel carriage became more complex in structure and more ornate in appearance as the 19th Century advanced. Pulled by hand, "jumpers," or two-wheel carriages, and arched four-wheel "spiders," were devised. Some companies experimented with two-cylinder carriages; the Southwark Hose Company in Philadelphia tried "The Twins," a double reel carriage. Each reel usually held four to six hundred feet of "hoase."

Original models of many hose reels, together with models of parade wagons, lend colorful interest to The Historical Collection. The early parade wagons, handsomely decorated, were hand-drawn, later developing into horse drawn vehicles similar to yesteryear's police patrol wagon.

1K • "B" HOSE REEL. Hand-made, hand-drawn, early type used in Brooklyn, N. Y. 1835.

2K • BINGHAMTON, N. Y. PARADE WAGON. Hand-made, hand-drawn, four bells, glass mirrors on sides.

3K • CHEMICAL & HOSE WAGON. Motorized. 1910.

4K • CITY HOSE COMPANY NO. 1, Boston, Mass. Hand-made, hand-drawn. 1820.

5K • CITY HOSE COMPANY NO. 1, New York City. Hand-made, hand-drawn.

6K • FAME HOSE REEL, Philadelphia. Hand-made, hand-drawn, solid silver model. 1830. (*Illustrated*).

7K • FRANKLIN FIRE COMPANY, Philadelphia. Hand-made, hand-drawn. 1830.

8K • HAND-IN-HAND HOSE COMPANY. Hand-made, hand-drawn. One of earliest hose reels used by volunteer firemen of Lancaster, Pa. 1820.

9K • HOPE HOSE COMPANY, Philadelphia. Sold to Wissahickon Fire Company in 1847—later sold to Pitman, N. J. Fire Company. 1837.

10K • HOSE REEL. Hand-made, hand-drawn. Used by N. Currier in the famous Currier & Ives lithographs, "The Life of a Fireman." 1835. (*Illustrated*).

11K • HOSE REEL. Hand-drawn. All-white model. 1835.

12K • HOSE REEL NO. 1. Hand-made, hand-drawn. 1800.

13K • HOSE REEL. Hand-made, hand-drawn. 1810.

14K • HOSE REEL. Hand-made, hand-drawn. All-white model, showing small candle lamps, crude springs. Primitive. 1828.

15K • HOSE REEL D. H. COMPANY. Hand-drawn. 1810.

16K • HOSE REEL NO. 1. Hand-made, hand-drawn, equipped with buckets, lamps, bell and tool box. 1830.

17K • HOSE REEL. Hand-made, hand-drawn. All-white model. 1835.

18K • HOSE REEL. Hand-made, hand-drawn. 1800.

19K • HOSE REEL. Hand-made, hand-drawn. Two wheels. 1835.

20K • HOSE REEL. Hand-made, hand-drawn, all-metal model. Equipped with buckets, lamps, lanterns and nozzles.

21K • HOSE REEL. Horse-drawn, set on base with motor attached. Type used in Johnstown, Pa. in 1885. This model was made by an old Volunteer in Johnstown, Pa.

22K • PHILADELPHIA HOSE COMPANY. Hand-made hand-drawn, early type hose reel. 1804. (*Illustrated*).

23K • HOSE REEL. Hand-made, hand-drawn, very rare type of model. 1800.

24K • HOSE COMPANY NO. 5 of New York. Horse-drawn.

25K • HOSE REEL AND CHEMICAL ENGINE. Hand-drawn. Working model. 1870.

26K • HOSE WAGON NO. 2. Combination salvage patrol truck, sled model. Hand-made, horse-drawn. 1868.

27K • JACKSON HOSE REEL. Hand-made, hand-drawn. 1835.

28K • JUNIATA PARADE WAGON. Hand-made, hand-drawn. Used by Juniata Volunteers of Pittsburgh, Pa. 1835.

29K • LIBERTY COMPANY HOSE REEL. Hand-drawn. 1835.

30K • LIBERTY HOSE REEL NO. 2. Hand-made, hand-drawn. 1800.

31K • "M" HOSE REEL. Hand-made, metal model marked "M".

32K • M.F.D. HOSE SLED. Horse-drawn, carrying ladders. Used in upper New England. The Hose Sled aided volunteer firemen in reaching fires on snowbound roads. 1865.

33K • MANCHESTER HOSE CARRIAGE NO. 1. Horse-drawn. Popular in New England from 1870 to 1885. This type of equipment was adopted by the first insurance patrols.

Model of the world's first hose cart used in 1804 by the Philadelphia Hose Company, and made after a design by Patrick Lyon, renowned engine builder. Hose was carried loosely in the oblong box structure.

34K • MIDDLESEX HOSE REEL. Hand-made, hand-drawn on sled runners. Used in New England States. 1860. (*Illustrated*).

35K • NEW YORK CITY NO. 33 H. R. Horse-drawn. Model includes horses. 1850.

36K • NEW YORK HOSE REEL NO. 42. Hand-made, hand-drawn. Painted red.

37K • NEW YORK CITY HOSE REEL. Hand-drawn. Reel is turtle-back type. These hose reels were attached to the old "hand tubs" and both pulled to the fire together. Equipment includes lanterns, axes, trumpet. 1812. (*Illustrated*).

38K • NEW ENGLAND PARADE WAGON. Hand-made, horse-drawn, with mirrors on sides. 1875.

39K • PARADE WAGON. Hand-made, solid silver; notable for its unusually fine workmanship. Models of parade wagons are very scarce. 1830.

40K • PARADE WAGON. Hand-made, hand-drawn. 1840.

41K • PARADE WAGON, Portland, Me. Hand-made, hand-drawn. 1830.

42K • PARADE WAGON, Providence, R. I. Hand-drawn. Mirrors on sides. 1835.

43K • PHILADELPHIA HOSE WAGON. Hand-made, hand-drawn. 1835.

44K • PITTSBURGH HOSE REEL. Hand-made, hand-drawn. 1825.

FULL SIZE HOSE REELS

45K • RESCUE HAND REEL. Hand-made, hand-drawn.

46K • SALEM, MASS. HOSE REEL. Hand-made, hand-drawn. 1835.

47K • SAN JOSE HOSE REEL. Hand-made, hand-drawn with bells and lamp. 1835.

48K • STAR HOSE REEL. Hand-drawn. 1840.

49K • STAR HOSE REEL. Hand-made, hand-drawn. 1800.

50K • SUFFOLK HOSE REEL. Hand-made, hand-drawn. New England parade wagon. Equipped with tool-box, candle lamp. Hand made glass is used on side of reel. 1845.

51K • UNION HOSE CARRIAGE. Hand-made, hand-drawn. 1834.

52K • UNION COMPANY NO. 1 HOSE REEL. Hand-made, hand-drawn. 1845.

53K • WASHINGTON COMPANY HOSE REEL. Hand-made, hand-drawn. Washington Company, Pittsburgh, Pa. 1835.

54K • WESTERN HOSE REEL. Hand-made, hand-drawn. 1835.

55K • WESTERN HOSE REEL. Hand-made, hand-drawn. 1825.

56K • WESTERN HOSE REEL. Hand-made, hand-drawn. 1825.

57K • WHITE CROWN HOSE REEL. Hand-made, hand-drawn New England Hose Reel. 1830.

58K • VETERAN HOSE REEL. Hand-drawn. 1838.

59K • PHILADELPHIA HOSE COMPANY. Hand-drawn, high wheel, unique type. 1795.

60K • UNITED STATES HOSE COMPANY REEL. Hand-drawn, built in 1820 by D. G. Matthews & Co., Philadelphia, Pa. This hose company was originally located at 6th & Walnut Sts. near site of first U. S. balloon ascension. Its hose reel was used in Philadelphia up to the institution of the paid fire department in 1870. 1820.

61K • HOPE HOSE COMPANY OF PHILADELPHIA. Hand-drawn. 1837.

Model of hand-drawn sledge, type of hose reel used in New England area, circa 1860. As early as 1783, Boston adopted sledges instead of wheels for fire engines during wintry weather.

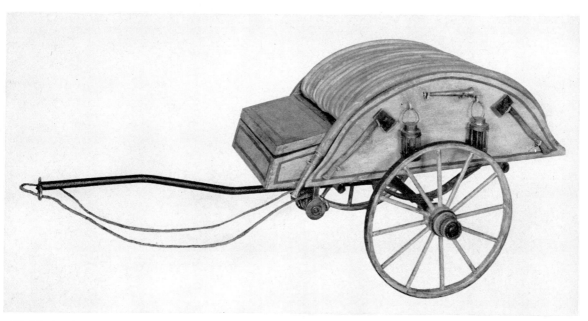

Model of early New York hose reel, turtle-back type, replete with lanterns, axes, and trumpet. This type was hitched to fire engine, and drawn tandem style to the fire. First New York hose company was founded in 1812.

THE AMERICAN FIREMAN,

Rushing to the Conflict

"*I remember his red shirt, his fireman's hat . . . and its prodigious rear extension of brim; his soap-lock, his trousers in his boots and his brass speaking-trumpet quite distinctly.*" "*Our Fire Laddies*": *J. Frank Kernan, 1885. (Print, entitled "Rushing to the Conflict," is a colored Currier & Ives in North America's Collection.)*

"Pull Heavy! Pull Together!"

ORDER, and even etiquette, governed the fire-fighting system even in volunteer days. And, the horn, a speaking trumpet, was the medium of conveying directions and shouting encouragement. The horns were carried by engineers, foremen, and their assistants. The foreman often ran ahead of the hand-drawn engine to ascertain the location of the fire, but when a race developed, he was alongside the engine, shouting zestfully: "Pull heavy! Pull together!"

When no water supply was near the fire, as frequently happened before the advent of the hydrant system, the first hand-pumper dropped its suction pump into a well, or river, and the second hand-pumper to arrive was asked by the foreman: "Will you take our water?"

Etiquette obliged an answer in the affirmative. Then the pumping began as subsequent arrivals formed a line from the water source to the fire. Shouts of "Man your brakes," "Start your water," were amplified by the "work horns." The pumping became fast and furious, sixty up and down strokes a minute, as relays of firemen manned the pumping levers, the object being to avoid disgrace by an overflowing reservoir, a sign that the pumpers had failed and the engine had been "washed."

Meantime, at the fire, the senior engineers lifted their horns to direct the fire-fighting . . . "Shake her up!" "Put a stream to the rear of the building!" . . . each engineer having charge of different phases of combating the fire.

The work horn was a symbol of authority, and, if a tempestuous occasion demanded, it could be used as a bludgeon. Its counterpart, for parade purposes and festive occasions, was the handsome silver horn usually presented by one company to another, or by members of a company to an honored chief.

The presentation horns are fine examples of the engraving art as well as being unique mementos that symbolize a chivalrous fraternity of public servants. It is said that on convivial evenings, the parade horn served as a drinking cup for a round-table salute to a guest, although many companies observed strict temperance rules.

In The Historical Collection are 126 horns of various sizes and kinds from many sections.

FIREMEN'S HORNS

1L • PARADE HORN, Silver Plated, 1869. Presented to Engine Company No. 3 of Paterson, N. J. by Columbia Guards of Newark, N. J.

2L • PARADE HORN, Silver Plated, 1881. Presented by Archie Graham to Passaic S. F. E. Company No. 1.

3L • PARADE HORN, Silver Plated, 1860. Presented to James W. Gaffney by his friends for his qualities as a fireman and his virtues as a citizen.

4L • PARADE HORN, Silver Plated, 1860. Presented by Jovial Club of Paterson, N. J. to Washington Fire Engine Company No. 3. (*Illustrated*).

5L • PARADE HORN, Silver Plated, 1890. Presented by Liberty S. F. E. Company No. 7 to Firemen's Exempt Association of Paterson, N. J.

6L • PARADE HORN, Silver Plated, 1872. Presented to James McGuire by Blackstone Hose Company No. 4

7L • PARADE HORN, Silver Plated, 1800. Presented by Morrisiana Hook and Ladder Company No. 1, Paterson, N. J. to Columbia Hose Company No. 1.

8L • PARADE HORN, Silver Plated, 1867. Presented to Neptune Engine Company No. 2 by Citizens of Paterson, N. J. through Josiah P. Doreninus.

9L • PARADE HORN, Silver Plated, 1838. Presented to Alexander Henry, Esq., President Hope Hose Company by members of the Company.

10L • PARADE HORN, Solid Silver, 1800. Presented to John Nesbitt, Esq. of the Hibernia Fire Company by the Insurance Company of North America.

11L • PARADE HORN, Brass, 1865. Presented to Phoenix Hose Company by the Juniors.

12L • PARADE HORN, Silver Plated, 1887. Presented to U. S. Fire Company of Atlantic City, N. J., by Washington Company No. 1, Coatesville, Pa.

13L • PARADE HORN, Silver Plated, 1876. Presented to Passaic Engine Company No. 1 by Neptune Guards of Newark, N. J.

14L • PARADE HORN, Silver Plated, 1865. Presented to Moyamensing Hose Company by Monumental Assembly.

15L • PARADE HORN, Silver Plated, 1857. Presented to Weccacoe Fire Company No. 5 by Citizens of Camden, N. J.

16L • PARADE HORN, Brass, 1862. Presented by Independence Hose Company No. 3, New York, to Henry K. Woodruff.

17L • PARADE HORN, 1886. Alert Hook and Ladder Company, Franklinville, N. Y.

18L • PARADE HORN, Silver Plated, 1840. American Hose Company.

19L • PARADE HORN, Silver Plated, 1800. Assistant Chief.

20L • PARADE HORN, Silver Plated. Assistant Foreman No. 2.

21L • PARADE HORN, Silver Plated, 1875. Assistant Foreman, H. & L. Company, Sing Sing, N. Y.

22L • PARADE HORN, Silver Plated, 1875. Auburn, N. Y.

23L • PARADE HORN, Silver Plated, 1800. Brooklyn, N. Y.

24L • PARADE HORN, Silver Plated, 1850. California.

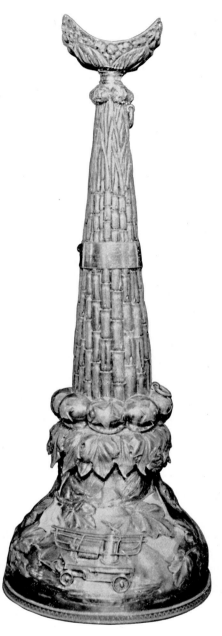

Showing signs of use, this brass speaking-trumpet aided the foreman to deliver orders in the din of crackling timbers and the tumult of men pumping at the fore and aft levers of a double-decker.

Silver and ornate, this type of speaking-horn was usually a gift from fire laddies to a well-respected officer of their company. On parade, the recipient of a silver horn carried it as a receptacle of a huge bouquet of flowers.

25L • PARADE HORN, Silver Plated, 1850. California.

26L • PARADE HORN, Silver Plated, 1885. California Fire Company.

27L • PARADE HORN, Silver Plated, 1865. Delaware Engine Company No. 4.

28L • PARADE HORN, Brass. Delaware Fire Company.

29L • PARADE HORN, Silver Plated, 1860. Engine Company No. 51, New York City.

30L • PARADE HORN, Silver Plated, 1878. Engine Company No. 36, New York.

31L • PARADE HORN, Silver Plated, 1886. Foreman, "John Weber."

32L • PARADE HORN, Silver Plated, 1886. Foreman No. 1.

33L • PARADE HORN, Silver Plated, 1850. Gaspee.

34L • PARADE HORN, Silver Plated, 1860. George W. Herbe.

35L • PARADE HORN, Silver Plated. Hope Engine Company, Philadelphia.

36L • PARADE HORN, Silver Plated, 1860. James Nolan, Philadelphia Hose Company No. 1.

37L • PARADE HORN, Silver Plated, 1820. Jackson Fire Company No. 24.

38L • PARADE HORN, Silver Plated, 1840. Jackson Fire Company No. 4, Paterson, N. J.

39L • PARADE HORN, Silver Plated, 1800. John A. Johnson, Lafayette Hose Company No. 22.

40L • PARADE HORN, Silver Plated, 1873. Kingston No. 2, New York City.

41L • PARADE HORN, Silver Plated, 1800. Lafayette.

42L • PARADE HORN, Silver Plated, 1878. Munger, New York City.

43L • PARADE HORN, Silver Plated, 1867. Neptune Engine Company No. 2, Paterson, N. J.

44L • PARADE HORN, Silver Plated, 1856. Ossining Hose Company, New York.

45L • PARADE HORN, Brass, 1806. Pennsylvania Fire Company.

46L • PARADE HORN, Silver Plated, 1805. Perseverance Hose No. 5.

47L • PARADE HORN, Silver Plated, 1877. Phinney Fire Company No. 4.

48L • PARADE HORN, Silver Plated. Ringgold Hose Company, Newburg, N. Y.

49L • PARADE HORN, Silver Plated, 1831. Robert Morris Hose Company, Philadelphia.

50L • PARADE HORN, Silver Plated. Second Assistant, Rapid No. 2, Worcester, Mass.

51L • PARADE HORN, Silver Plated. Tompkins Hose Company No. 16, New York.

52L • PARADE HORN, Silver Plated, 1832. Washington Engine Company, Philadelphia.

53L • PARADE HORN, Silver Plated, 1832. Washington Engine Company No. 3, Philadelphia.

54L • PARADE HORN, Silver Plated, 1869.

55L • PARADE HORN, Silver Plated, 1881.

56L • WORK HORN, Silver Plated. Leather Handle.

57L • WORK HORN, Silver Plated. Leather Handle.

58L • WORK HORN, Brass, 1750.

59L • WORK HORN, Brass, 1750.

60L • WORK HORN, Brass, 1800.

61L • WORK HORN, Brass, 1810.

62L • WORK HORN, Brass, 1820. Squire Edwin Onyx.

63L • WORK HORN, Brass, 1830. (Illustrated).

64L • WORK HORN, Brass, 1830.

65L • WORK HORN, Brass, 1835.

66L • WORK HORN, Brass, 1835.

67L • WORK HORN, Brass, 1840.

68L • WORK HORN, Brass, 1840.

69L • WORK HORN, Brass, 1845.

70L • WORK HORN, Brass, 1850.

71L • WORK HORN, 1855. Leather Covered.

72L • WORK HORN, Brass, 1865.

73L • WORK HORN, Copper.

74L-126L • UNIDENTIFIED. Work Horns of Various Sizes. No Names.

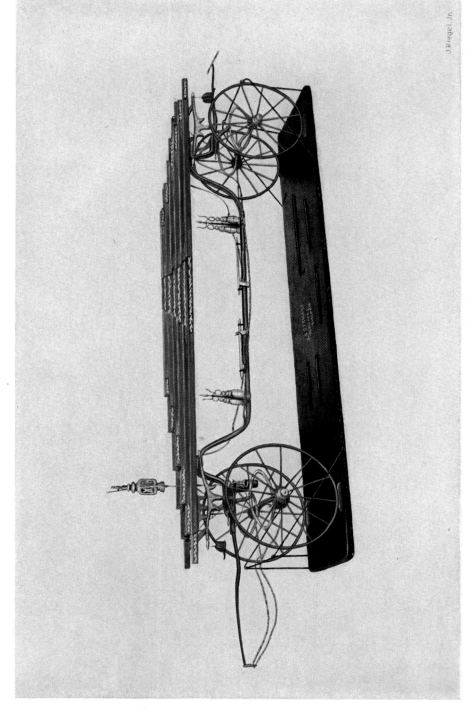

J. Riegel, Jr.

Many volunteer firemen were skilled at the hobby of shaping and building accurate miniature models of their fire engines. Above represents one of more than two score hook-and-ladder models in North America's Collection.

"Men Up to the Roof"

IN days of antiquity, the sheer walls of mighty bastions were scaled by soldiers using hooks and ladders. These implements, as we might expect, were converted to the peacetime use of fire-fighting. And, in our time, when men have built skyward, the hook and ladder engines, as used by modern firemen, are more effective than ever.

When the colonists settled along the seaboard of America, hooks and ladders made an immediate appearance. In 1659 "six substantiall ladders and three iron hookes" were ordered at Boston for community use, to be hung in a public place. Shortly after the Quakers founded Philadelphia, the Common Council ordered "Twenty Ladders, and Twenty-five Hooks, with axes."

In New York City, even after the 19th Century had been reached, Hook and Ladder Company No. 1 kept its hooks and ladders hanging in the main passageway of the City Hall in Wall Street, and carried them without trucks to fires.

Hooks and ladders of early American companies were frequently adjuncts to engine and hose apparatus but, in many cities, hook and ladder companies were formed, their members securing beautifully decorated carriages with 40-foot ladders, embellished with handsome scrollwork, and equipped with the usual complement of hooks, picks and axes. In The North America's Historical Collection, a wide range of hook and ladder apparatus is represented in original, old models.

The hook and ladder men were proud of their calling. The cry of "Men up to the roof!" at a fire was a challenge only for the brave. The brilliant record of lives saved and fires thwarted by hook and ladder firemen continues in the fire-fighting profession today.

1M • BROOKLYN HOOK AND LADDER. Hand-made, hand-drawn marked "B" with bust of George Washington. 1815.

2M • COLUMBIA HOOK AND LADDER COMPANY. Hand-made, hand-drawn. Philadelphia, Pa. 1825.

3M • EAGLE HOOK AND LADDER COMPANY. Hand-made, hand-drawn. 1838.

4M • EAGLE HOOK AND LADDER COMPANY. Hand-made, horse-drawn. Paterson, N. J. 1840.

5M • EMPIRE HOOK AND LADDER. Hand-made, hand-drawn. Made from original piece of fire-fighting apparatus used in New York City. Fully equipped with tool box, wall and ceiling hooks, lanterns, axes and buckets. 1815.

6M • EMPIRE VOLUNTEER FIRE COMPANY, Philadelphia. Hand-made, hand-drawn. 1840.

7M • HAYES HOOK AND LADDER. Horse-drawn, aerial hook and ladder. 1890.

8M • HIBERNIA NO. 6, Allentown, Pa. One of first motorized, right-hand drive, hand-aerials. Made of cardboard and basil wood. Built in Allentown, Pa. 1900.

9M • HOOK AND LADDER. Hand-made, hand-drawn, equipped with tallow-burning torch, four wooden buckets, four ladders, four hooks, horn, 2 hats. Very rare model. 1815.

10M • HOOK AND LADDER. Hand-made, hand-drawn, includes small leather buckets and hats. 1815.

11M • HOOK AND LADDER. Hand-made, horse-drawn with pivot and extension. Obtained in Alexandria, Va. 1895. (*Illustrated*).

12M • HOOK AND LADDER. Hand-made, primitive model. 1825.

13M • HOOK AND LADDER. Hand-drawn. Auxiliary to Hand Pumper, equipped with lamps, buckets, axes and hooks. 1816.

14M • HOOK AND LADDER. Hand-made, hand-drawn, equipped with buckets, lamps and hats.

15M • HOOK AND LADDER NO. 1. Horse-drawn sled model, equipped with wall and ceiling hooks, axes, ladders, maul, bell and extinguishers. Used in New England in winter. 1875.

16M • HOOK AND LADDER. Hand-made, horse-drawn, painted black and yellow. 1885.

17M • HOOK AND LADDER. Hand-made, hand-drawn. 1830.

18M • HOOK AND LADDER. Hand-made, hand-drawn. 1800.

19M • HOOK AND LADDER NO. 2. Hand-drawn, sled-type used in upper New England. 1815.

20M • HOOK AND LADDER. Hand-made, hand-drawn. 1800.

21M • HOOK AND LADDER. Hand-made, horse-drawn on sled runners. Used in upper New England. 1860.

22M • HOOK AND LADDER. Working model of first pneumatic aerial hook and ladder wagons. One filling of air in compression tank, at base of model, is ample to raise and hold the ladder many times. The tongue for the horses is believed to have been lost at St. Louis, Mo., one of the many places it was on exhibition. The first large truck made from this model was in 1900 by the International Fire Company, now part of the American-LaFrance-Foamite Corporation, of Elmira, N. Y., for the Cleveland, O. Fire Department. Other large hook and ladders of a horse-drawn type were made from this patented model and sold to Newark, N. J., St. Louis, Mo., Dallas, Tex., and Philadelphia at an average cost of $7,000 each. 1899.

23M • HOOK AND LADDER NO. 1, Pittsburgh, Pa. Hand-made, hand-drawn, equipped with oil lamps, buckets and a megaphone used for calling orders at fires. 1820.

24M • HOOK AND LADDER. Hand-made, aerial, pneumatic tires. Drawn by three horses. 1890.

25M • HOOK AND LADDER. Hand-made, hand-drawn, equipped with lamps, axes and hooks. 1815.

26M • HOOK AND LADDER TRUCK NO. 3. Hand-made, horse-drawn. This model was presented to Chief White, of Lancaster, Pa. in 1918 in honor of his fifty years of service with the fire department. 1885.

THE LIFE OF A FIREMAN.

An 1854 N. Currier lithograph. Drawing by Louis Maurer shows dramatic scene of a fire with hook and ladder men in action. Largest truck in New York at this time, the Friendship's, carried seven ladders.

27M • HOOK AND LADDER WAGON. Hand-drawn. Illustrates early use of raising and lowering device, and extension ladder. Equipped with large lamp on standard. 1835.

28M • HOOK AND LADDER WAGON. Hand-drawn, equipped with oil torches, buckets, wall and ceiling hooks. 1840.

29M • HOPE COMPANY HOOK AND LADDER. Hand-made, hand-drawn.

30M • HUBBS, NEW YORK HOOK AND LADDER. Hand-made, hand-drawn. Very early type. 1810.

31M • LINCOLN HOOK AND LADDER. Hand-drawn, marked "Lincoln 1865" with bells, hooks, buckets, and torches. 1865.

32M • MIDDLESEX HOOK AND LADDER. Hand-made, hand-drawn with wall and ceiling hooks, buckets, top hat, ladders, etc. 1815.

33M • MT. GUYOT HOOK AND LADDER. Hand-made, horse-drawn, sled model with eleven ladders, axes, hammers, hooks, door opener, and other volunteer equipment. Used in upper New England. 1863.

34M • NEWMARKET HOOK AND LADDER. Accurate copy of original apparatus pulled to fire in rear of hand pumper. Original of this model was in use in Schuylkill Co., Pa. as late as Civil War days. 1804.

35M • NEW YORK HOOK AND LADDER No. 6. Hand-made, horse-drawn.

36M • N. H. HOOK AND LADDER. Hand-made, horse-drawn sled type used in upper New England, particularly in New Hampshire. 1865.

37M • OIL CITY HOOK AND LADDER. Hand-made, hand-drawn, equipped with candle lamp on standard, torch, hats, buckets, ladders, wall and ceiling hooks. 1815.

38M • RESCUE HOOK AND LADDER. Hand-made, hand-drawn. 1815.

39M • RESCUE HOOK AND LADDER No. 5. Hand-made, horse-drawn of Allentown, Pa. 1881.

40M • SENECA FALLS, N. Y. Horse-drawn hook and ladder. This model was used as a salesman's sample and was carried from one community to another. 1865.

41M • SHACKAMAXON HOOK AND LADDER. Hand-made, hand-drawn. 1815.

42M • SOUTH CAMDEN HOOK AND LADDER. Hand-powered, aerial hook and ladder. Motor driven with left-hand drive. 1920.

43M • STAR HOOK AND LADDER. Hand-drawn. 1815.

44M • STAR HOOK AND LADDER. Hand-made, hand-drawn. Original used in Brooklyn, N. Y. 1815 to 1835.

45M • TIGER HOOK AND LADDER. Hand-drawn. 1815.

46M • UNION HOOK AND LADDER. Hand-drawn. 1825.

47M • VOLUNTEER HOOK AND LADDER No. 1. First motorized rescue and salvage truck with right hand drive. 1904.

48M • WASHINGTON FIRE ENGINE COMPANY. Hand-made, hand-drawn hook and ladder built by S. B. Stewart. 1816.

49M • WASHINGTON HOOK AND LADDER No. 1. Hand-made, hand-drawn, hook and ladder, Brooklyn. 1820.

50M • WASHINGTON HOOK AND LADDER. Hand-made, hand-drawn, oil torches, hats and buckets marked "W". 1815.

51M • WASHINGTON VOLUNTEER FIRE COMPANY. Hand-made, hand-drawn hook and ladder, can be drawn from either end. 1820.

52M • WATERBURY, CONN. HOOK AND LADDER. Hand-made, hand-drawn model of first hook and ladder used in Waterbury. 1815.

FULL SIZE HOOK AND LADDERS

53M • HOOK AND LADDER. Hand-drawn. 1810.

54M • PHILADELPHIA FIRE COMPANY. Hand-drawn. Practically the first hook and ladder used in Philadelphia. Built for the Philadelphia Fire Company as its first piece of equipment, when it was organized in 1799. Sold to a Delaware Company in 1825 and used by that company until 1850, and thereafter preserved in its original form. Entire equipment is original and includes hats, picks, ladders, axes, buckets, whale oil torches, etc. 1799. (*Illustrated*).

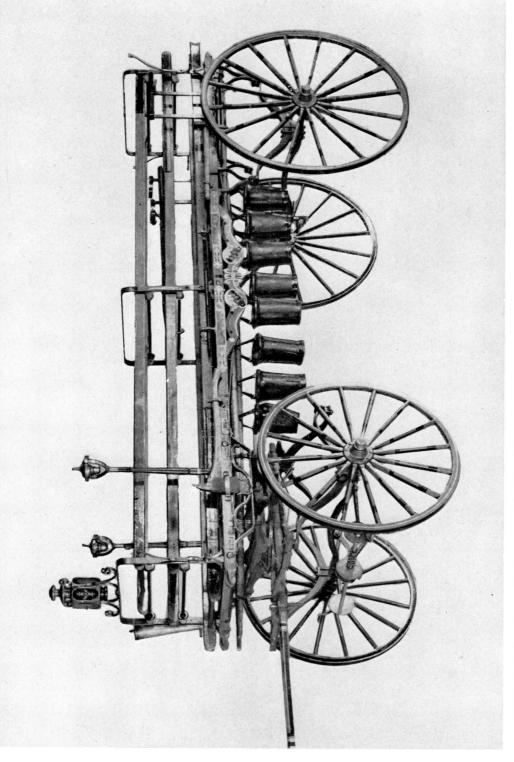

Full size hand-drawn hook and ladder truck used in Philadelphia during 1799. Built for the Philadelphia Fire Company, it is preserved today complete with its original whale-oil torches, buckets, axes, and ladders.

"No, the old hat don't make much show, but it's business all over. If a brick strikes anywhere on the hat, it bounds right off: but if it wasn't for that heavy hat, where'd you be?" A New York Fireman, 1880. (Lithograph by Currier & Ives, in North America's Collection.)

Head-Wear at the Fire

FIRE hats were worn in early days as a means of identification. The first fire hat to be adopted in Boston, for example, was a black leather jockey-cap with a pewter badge bearing the number of the fire company. This was in 1764, more than two decades after Jacob Turck, a gunsmith and "Overseer of Fire Engines," in New York City, is reputed to have devised the first fire hat, a round hat of stove-pipe shape with a narrow brim. This type of hat, employing a black brim and white crown, was adopted as regulation by Philadelphia firemen in 1788.

Fire hats evolved into protective head-pieces during the 19th Century, thereby anticipating the modern military helmet. The fire helmet not only protected the fireman against water and fallen debris but was a handy instrument in emergencies. Moreover, it served as a shield for his face when facing smoke and flame.

Perhaps the greatest innovator in the field of making fire hats was Henry T. Gratacap, of New York, who established a business at 329 Broadway in 1836. At Gratacap's establishment, a gathering place for fire laddies, this notable hat-maker designed a head-piece for one Ebenezer Silleck, engine company foreman. It was embellished with raised white letters stitched upon a black leather background, the first "raised front" hat. Gratacap himself was a fireman, and in 1858 was foreman of the Columbian Company at the burning of the Crystal Palace on the site of what is now Bryant Park in New York City.

The rearward extension of the brim seen in modern fire helmets is a feature of fire hats used more than a century ago. It is possible that this style evolved from the early jockey-cap type worn in reverse as an attempt to prevent water from running down the back of the fireman's neck.

In The Historical Collection, many interesting examples of "work hats," the kind actually worn in fire-fighting, come from different sections of the nation.

FIREMEN'S WORK HATS

1N-2N • AMERICAN HOSE NO. 2. 1828.

3N-4N • AMERICAN HOSE NO. 2. 1840.

5N • A. R. W. NO. 19. 1860.

6N • ASSISTANT. 1880.

7N • ASSISTANT CHIEF D. S. F. 1845.

8N • ASSISTANT CHIEF. 1845.

9N • ASSISTANT CHIEF, Paterson, N. J. 1850.

10N • ASSISTANT CHIEF ENGINEER (white hat). 1845.

11N • ASSISTANT CHIEF ENGINEER. 1845.

12N • ASSISTANT CHIEF. 1810.

13N-14N • ASSISTANCE NO. 8. 1840.

15N • ASSISTANT CHIEF. 1772.

16N • ASSISTANT HOSE COMPANY NO. 2. 1870.

17N • ATLANTA. 1859.

18N • B. F. D. NO. 1. 1835.

19N • CANANDAIGUA NO. 3. 1830.

20N • CATARACT HOSE CO. 1838.

21N • CATARACT NO. 2. 1840.

22N • CHARLESTOWN, MASS. NO. 1. 1842.

23N • CHARLESTOWN VETERANS. 1842.

24N • CHIEF. 1865.

25N • CHIEF ENGINEER, Chelsea, Mass. 1860.

26N • CHIEF ENGINEER, Boston, Mass. 1842.

27N • CHIEF ENGINEER, Paterson, N. J. 1884.

28N • CHIEF ENGINEER, C. F. D. 1875.

29N • CHIEF ENGINEER, F. C., D. M. L. 1875.

30N • CITIZEN NO. 3. 1836.

31N • CLERK NO. 5, J. F. D., Paterson, N. J. 1880.

32N • CLABE FIRE COMPANY NO. 3. 1870.

33N • COLUMBIA. 1806.

34N • COLUMBIA. 1806.

35N • COLUMBIA NO. 5, F. D. 1806 (*Illustrated*).

36N • CONTINENTAL. 1845.

37N • DENVER FIRE COMPANY. 1815.

38N • DUNMORE. 1885.

39N • EAGLE, Lynn, Mass. 1840.

40N • EAGLE NO. 2, Hanover, Pa. 1845.

41N • EDWIN FORREST HOSE NO. 5. 1860.

42N • ENGINE COMPANY NO. 2, Los Angeles, Cal. 1840.

43N • ENGINE COMPANY NO. 5, L. F. D. 1849.

44N • EXCELSIOR NO. 6. 1851.

45N • F. A. (large white hat). 1800.

46N • FAIR HAVEN V. F. D. NO. 1. 1860.

47N • FAIRMOUNT NO. 32. 1832.

48N • FELLOWSHIP FIRE CO., NO. 27, S. F. D. 1819.

49N • FOREMAN, Trenton, N. J. 1820.

50N • FOREMAN, EXCELSIOR. 1850.

51N • FOREMAN NO. 1. 1810. (*Illustrated*).

52N • FRIENDSHIP FIRE COMPANY, Philadelphia. 1796.

53N-55N • FRIENDSHIP HOSE COMPANY. 1847.

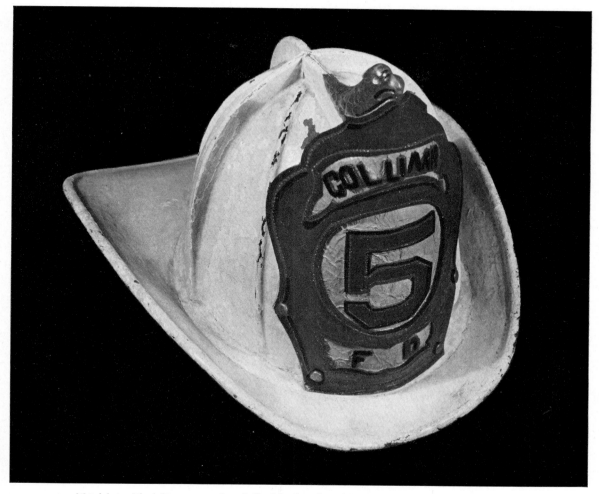

Metal hat with eight seams, or "combs." Metal eagle and leather shield were popular ornaments.

56N • Franklin Hook and Ladder No. 1. 1815.

57N • G. L. B. (tin hat). 1835.

58N • Germantown Fire Company. 1825.

59N • Good Intent, Pottsville, Pa. 1840.

60N • Good Will Company, Germantown, Pa. 1813.

61N • Good Will Fire Company, C. B. 1802.

62N • Good Will Fire Company. 1845.

63N • Good Will Hose Company No. 25. 1813.

64N • H. K. W. Vol. Assn., N. Y. 1845.

65N • Hand-in-Hand. 1772.

66N • Harmony. 1880.

67N • Hook and Ladder Company No. 3, New Orleans. 1850.

68N • Hook and Ladder Company No. 6, Newark, N. J. 1865.

69N • Hook and Ladder Company No. 15, San Pedro, Cal. 1825.

70N • Hope Engine Company No. 1. 1800.

71N-72N • Hope Hose Company. 1805.

73N • Hoseman No. 1. 1820.

74N • HOSEMAN NO. 2, L. F. D., Lowell, Mass. 1850.

75N • HOSEMAN NO. 5. 1820.

76N • INDEPENDENCE FIRE COMPANY. 1848.

77N • INDEPENDENCE FIRE COMPANY NO. 1. 1848.

78N • JOHN W. BAIRD, R. F. D. NO. 5. 1855.

79N • J. J. ROWE, OSSINING HOSE COMPANY, N. Y. 1886.

80N-81N • LADDER NO. 5, L. F. D. 1849.

82N • LAFAYETTE HOSE. 1833.

83N • LIBERTY NO. 5, Paterson, N. J. 1805.

84N • MANAYUNK FIRE COMPANY. 1838.

85N • MECHANIC FIRE COMPANY. 1825.

86N • MITCHELL HOSE COMPANY. 1825.

87N-88N • MOYAMENSING HOSE COMPANY. 1837.

89N • MOYAMENSING NO. 1. 1837.

90N • NASHUA. 1850.

91N-92N • NEPTUNE HOSE COMPANY. 1805.

93N-94N • NEW ENGLAND. 1860.

95N-96N • NEWTON, MASS. FIRE COMPANY NO. 1. 1800.

97N-98N • NIAGARA. 1827.

99N • NORTHERN LIBERTY HOSE COMPANY. 1828.

100N • NO. 1, F. D. 1860.

101N • NO. 2, F. D. 1796.

102N • NO. 3, F. D. 1846.

103N • NO. 6, F. D. 1850.

104N • NO. 9, F. D. 1845.

105N • NO. 78. 1860.

106N • PACIFIC NO. 28. 1865.

107N • PELHAM. 1800.

108N • PHILADELPHIA VETERANS. 1870.

109N • PHOENIX HOSE COMPANY. 1845.

110N • PIONEER NO. 11. 1865.

111N • PLAINFIELD NO. 2. 1870.

112N • PROVIDENCE, R. I., VOLUNTEERS. 1865.

113N • RAPID HOSE COMPANY. 1819.

114N • READING NO. 1819.

115N • RED HOOK FIRE COMPANY. 1850.

116N • RESOLUTION HOSE COMPANY NO. 3. 1804.

117N • RINGGOLD HOSE COMPANY. 1805.

118N • SACO. 1850. (*Illustrated*).

119N • SAN FRANCISCO FIRE DEPT. 1875.

120N • SCHUYLKILL HOSE COMPANY NO. 24. 1815.

121N • SECOND ASST. ENGINEER. 1865.

122N • SOUTH PENN NO. 31. 1864.

123N • SOUTHWARK NO. 9. 1827.

124N • SPRING GARDEN FIRE COMPANY NO. 3. 1820.

125N • STOCKTON NO. 2. 1855.

126N • SUN FIRE COMPANY. 1778.

127N • TIGER NO. 6, Worcester. 1830.

128N • TRENTON HOSE COMPANY NO. 1. 1840.

129N-130N • UNION FIRE COMPANY. 1736.

131N • VOLUNTEER HOSE COMPANY NO. 1. 1845.

132N-133N • VOLUNTEER OF PHILADELPHIA. 1845.

134N • VOLUNTEER FIREMEN'S ASSN. OF PATERSON, N. J. 1830.

135N • VETERANS, Hartford, Conn. 1870.

136N • VETERAN NO. 3, Worcester, F. A. 1819.

137N • WASHINGTON ENGINE COMPANY NO. 1. 1820.

138N • WASHINGTON FIRE COMPANY. 1793.

139N • WASHINGTON HOSE COMPANY NO. 2. 1840.

140N • WASHINGTON (red hat). 1840.

141N • WASHINGTON NO. 4. 1820.

142N • WESTERN HOSE COMPANY. 1860.

143N • W. D. NO. 12. 1840.

144N-162N • UNIDENTIFIED.

Early hat made entirely of leather, with four hand-sewed "combs," and hand-painted flourishes on brim.

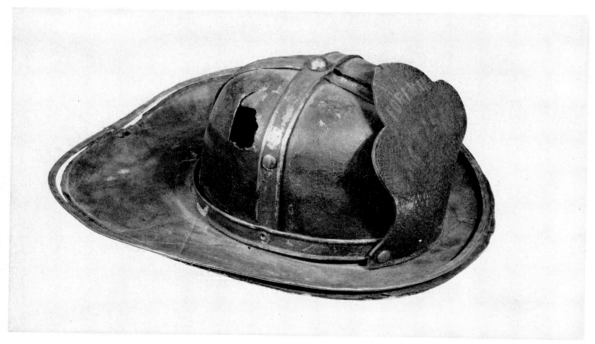

Foreman's hat of mid-19th Century, showing evidence of use. Comprised of leather crown and brim with iron riveted segments and leather hat shield.

HIBERNIA FIRE ENGINE COMPANY. N°1.
OF PHILADELPHIA.

Illustration from rare 1857 Duval print in North America's Collection shows men of the Hibernia Company, of Philadelphia, in their green decorated parade hats and capes. Hibernia's Engine House is in background.

Fire Hats on Parade

WHEN the Marquis de Lafayette arrived in 1824, a gala parade of firemen from Manhattan and Brooklyn added to the warm welcome tendered to the gallant Frenchman upon his visit to these shores. In 1832, at the Centennial celebration of Washington's birthday, the firemen of Philadelphia held their first parade.

During the middle decades of the last century, colorful processions of this kind were held in many cities. Fire companies visited from city to city on these occasions, competing in personal dress and engine display for the plaudits of the crowds which thronged the flag-draped streets. So great was the participation during the firemen's parade of 1859 in Manhattan, several hours were required for the marchers to pass a single point.

During these colorful reviews, the fire trucks were decorated with flowers, bunting, and even animals, while the firemen themselves were adorned in parade uniforms of various hues and designs.

On parade, the fireman put aside his "work helmet" and donned a handsome hat. These parade hats were frequently painted with company colors, decorated with insignia, and glazed with varnish.

On parade, it was not unusual for engineers and foremen to wear presentation hats; these frequently were emblazoned with ornamental shields of ornate leather and metal craftsmanship. Gratacap, the famed fire hat designer, once made a presentation hat with a badge of gold and silver in which precious stones were set. The jeweler's bill alone for this hat was $850. Presented by the firemen of Sacramento, California to their foreman, this hat set a record for costliness.

In The Historical Collection are many parade hats, vivid emblems of the storied pageantry that was dear to the hearts of the firemen. Wearing their "dress hats" and parade uniforms, they marched with their engines and flying banners to the martial music of the brass brand. At a blaze or at a parade, the volunteer was proud of his calling.

P A R A D E   H A T S

1 O • ALLEGHENY FIRE COMPANY. 1802.

2 O • CITIZENS FIRE COMPANY. 1836.

3 O • COLUMBIA FIRE COMPANY. 1796. (*Illustrated*).

4 O • COLUMBIA FIRE COMPANY. C.E.C. 1796.

5 O • COLUMBIA HOSE COMPANY. J.M.I. C.H.C. 1806.

6 O • DECATUR FIRE ENGINE COMPANY. J.B.A. 1790.

7 O • DECATUR FIRE COMPANY. 1790. (*Illustrated*).

8 O • DILIGENT FIRE COMPANY. A.P.M. 1791.

9 O • DILIGENT HOSE COMPANY. 1820.

10 O • EAGLE FIRE COMPANY. A.C. 1821.

11 O • EAGLE HOSE COMPANY. 1851.

12 O • EAGLE FIRE COMPANY. 1821.

13 O • EAGLE FIRE COMPANY. 1821.

14 O • FAIRMOUNT FIRE ASSOCIATION. 1847.

15 O • FAIR MOUNT HOSE COMPANY. 1847.

16 O • FAIRMOUNT FIRE COMPANY OF PHILADELPHIA. 1823.

17 O • FAIR MOUNT HOSE COMPANY. 1847.

18 O • FRANKLIN FIRE COMPANY No. 4, "Haste to the Rescue." 1792.

19 O • FRANKLIN HOSE COMPANY. 1838.

20 O • FRIENDSHIP FIRE COMPANY. 1839.

21 O • FRIENDSHIP FIRE COMPANY. 1839.

22 O • FRIENDSHIP HOSE COMPANY. 1847.

23 O • FRIENDSHIP FIRE COMPANY. 1839.

24 O • FRIENDSHIP HOSE COMPANY. 1847.

25 O • GLOBE FIRE COMPANY. W.R. 1820.

26 O • GOOD WILL FIRE COMPANY. 1802. (*Illustrated*).

27 O • GOOD WILL FIRE COMPANY. 1802.

28 O • GERMANTOWN HOSE COMPANY No. 1. 1848.

29 O • HAND-IN-HAND FIRE COMPANY, Philadelphia. C.B.C. 1790.

30 O • HAND-IN-HAND FIRE COMPANY. 1790.

31 O • HARMONY FIRE COMPANY. C.P.S. 1849.

32 O • HARMONY FIRE COMPANY. 1840.

33 O • HARMONY FIRE COMPANY No. 6. 1849.

34 O • HOPE HOSE COMPANY, Philadelphia. R.W.J. 1805.

35 O • HOPE HOSE COMPANY. 1805.

36 O • HOPE HOSE COMPANY. 1805.

37 O • HOPE FIRE COMPANY. J.J.S. 1796.

38 O • HOPE HOSE COMPANY. 1805.

39 O • HOPE VOLUNTEER FIRE COMPANY. 1796.

40 O • HUMANE FIRE COMPANY. 1797.

41 O • HIBERNIA FIRE COMPANY. 1752.

42 O • HIBERNIA FIRE COMPANY. 1752.

43 O • HOWARD FIRE COMPANY No. 15, Baltimore. "We Conquer to Save." 1790.

Members of Decatur Company, of Frankford district in Philadelphia, wore parade hats ornamented with portraits of their namesake.

Columbia Company, located in historic Germantown section of Philadelphia, wore this type of hat in line of march. Hats were glazed with varnish.

Good Will Hose Company, of Philadelphia, adopted this parade hat. Colored vermilion, with lettering and star hand-colored in gold.

44 O • JUNIOR NO. 2. 1813.

45 O • KENSINGTON FIRE COMPANY NO. 1. J.F. 1791.

46 O • KEYSTONE HOOK AND LADDER COMPANY. 1852.

47 O • LAFAYETTE HOSE COMPANY. 1833.

48 O • MANSFIELD NO. 1.

49 O • MONROE FIRE COMPANY. J.F. 1823.

50 O • MONROE FIRE COMPANY. 1823.

51 O • MARION HOSE COMPANY. J.H.H. 1833.

52 O • MORRIS HOSE COMPANY. 1831.

53 O • NEPTUNE HOSE COMPANY. J.D.C. 1805.

54 O • NEPTUNE HOSE COMPANY. 1805.

55 O • NORRISTOWN HOSE COMPANY. J.B.T. 1847.

56 O • NORTHERN LIBERTY HOSE COMPANY. J.H.H. 1828.

57 O • NORTHERN LIBERTY FIRE COMPANY. 1796.

58 O • NORTHERN LIBERTY FIRE COMPANY NO. 1. 1796.

59 O • PENNSYLVANIA HOSE COMPANY. C.H.H. 1818.

60 O • PENNSYLVANIA HOSE COMPANY. 1818.

61 O • PENNSYLVANIA VOLUNTEER FIRE COMPANY. 1790.

62 O • PERSEVERANCE HOSE COMPANY NO. 5. J.P.W. 1805.

63 O • PHILADELPHIA HOSE COMPANY NO. 1. J.S.M. 1803.

64 O • PHOENIX HOSE COMPANY. W.F. 1817.

65 O • RAINBOW FIRE COMPANY NO. 1. 1773.

66 O • SCHUYLKILL HOSE COMPANY NO. 24. 1833.

67 O • SHIFFLER HOSE COMPANY NO. 1. G.H.M. 1846.

68 O • TAYLOR HOSE COMPANY. 1848.

69 O • TAYLOR HOSE COMPANY. 1848.

70 O • TORRENT HOSE COMPANY NO. 2. 1790.

71 O • UNION FIRE COMPANY. 1819.

72 O • UNION HOSE COMPANY. 1760.

73 O • UNITED STATES FIRE COMPANY. 1811.

74 O • UNITED STATES FIRE COMPANY. 1860.

75 O • VETERANS, Hartford, Conn.

76 O • VIGILANT FIRE COMPANY. 1760.

77 O • VIGILANT FIRE COMPANY, Baltimore, Md. J.R. 1830.

78 O • WASHINGTON FIRE COMPANY NO. 14. S.J. 1796.

79 O • WASHINGTON COMPANY, Paterson, N. J. 1820.

80 O • WASHINGTON FIRE COMPANY. J.L.H. 1796.

81 O • WESTERN ENGINE COMPANY. D.S. 1840.

82 O • WESTERN HOSE COMPANY. 1836.

83 O • WILLIAM PENN HOSE COMPANY. J.H.C. 1830.

84 O • WILLIAM PENN HOSE COMPANY. 1830.

85 O • WILLIAM PENN HOSE COMPANY. 1830.

"Oyl Cloth" and Canvas

CAPES were worn by firemen to protect them when water and embers fell upon their shoulders. Moreover, capes served to identify firemen during the inevitable bustle which attended the outbreak of fires. In many cities, however, capes with decorations were worn principally during parades.

Among the first capes to be worn by American firemen were those donned in 1794 by the engineers of the Assistance Fire Company, Philadelphia, a group composed mainly of young men who attended Zion and St. Michael's Lutheran Churches.

These early capes were made of "oyl cloth," but, in the following century, capes were made in one piece of canvas and treated with three heavy layers of paint. The cape was usually painted in the company's colors and, as in the case of fire-hats, usually bore the date of the company's founding.

Many capes were decorated with symbolic illustrations by local artists who painted signs, engine-sides, and fire hats. Many capes are said to have been embellished by the deft brush of John A. Woodside.

As in the case of fire hats and engine sides these decorations have a unique place in the popular American arts which gave us form and color in glassware, pottery, ships' figureheads, and samplers. When the volunteer embellished his cape, he was infusing his individual expression with a part of his daily life. If his designs were colorful, and even boisterous, it must be remembered that the fireman's life has never been dull. Indeed, the visual arts in the period of volunteer fire-fighting stemmed from the same creative force that produced new inventions for mankind's use.

During engine contests, as shown in this 1850 event held at 5th and Market Streets in Philadelphia, firemen wore their fancy parade capes. Drawing of this demonstration was made by Charles H. Spieler.

FIREMEN'S CAPES

1P • AMERICAN EAGLE. 1811.

2P • AMERICAN FIRE ASSOCIATION. 1830.

3P • AMERICAN HOSE COMPANY. 1828.

4P • COLUMBIA HOSE COMPANY. 1763.

5P • DELAWARE ENGINE COMPANY. 1761.

6P • EAGLE HOSE COMPANY NO. 3. 1851.

7P • FAIR MOUNT HOSE COMPANY. 1847.

8P • FRIENDSHIP FIRE COMPANY, Alexandria, Va. 1775.

9P • GOOD WILL. 1804.

10P • HAND-IN-HAND FIRE COMPANY. 1772.

11P • LAFAYETTE HOSE COMPANY. 1833.

12P • PHILADELPHIA FIRE COMPANY. 1799.

13P • SHIFFLER HOSE COMPANY. 1846.

14P • UNION FIRE COMPANY. 1747.

15P • UNITED STATES HOSE COMPANY. 1807.

16P • WESTERN HOSE COMPANY. 1840.

George Washington is said to have owned this cape as honorary member of the Friendship Fire Company of Alexandria, Virginia, organized circa 1775. Cape is very heavily painted cloth.

"Translation of Psyche," showing that mythological beauty being taken to the immortals on Olympus, was the work of John Archibald Woodside, of Philadelphia (1781-1854). This panel was the pride of the Americus Company No. 6 of New York City, also known as The Tiger. "Boss" Tweed was once foreman of this company.

Art and the Fireman

ENGINE sides, the wide panels attached to hand-drawn engines for decoration, were frequently painted by artists of considerable standing in early days. They were affixed to the galleries on the condensing cases which usually surmounted the machines in box-like structures. Today these painted panels are museum pieces.

The Historical Collection is enriched by the possession of two engine panels painted by Thomas Sully, whose paintings, each valued at many thousands of dollars, are in the great art museums of the nation. Sully, born in the very year of North America's founding, achieved success at an early age, and, in 1821, was commissioned to paint a full length figure of Thomas Jefferson for the United States Military Academy at West Point. His portrait of Lafayette, painted from life, is one of the notable canvases to be seen today at Independence Hall in Philadelphia.

Another artist whose engine side paintings add to the distinguished group in The Historical Collection is John A. Woodside. A Philadelphia historian in 1884 wrote of Woodside: "His frontispieces for hose carriages, side and front and rear gallery paintings for fire-engines, were beautiful." Most critics, even today, give him a place in American art although Woodside employed most of his time as a commercial painter. The North America was proud to have its Woodside panels appear in a recent exhibition at the Philadelphia Museum of Art together with paintings by Woodside owned by Mrs. John D. Rockefeller, noted connoisseur of early American art.

A contemporary of Sully and Woodside, David Rent Etter is represented among North America's panels in the Museum of the City of New York. These panels graced the pumper of Philadelphia's Franklin Engine Company which arrived in New York for duty during the fire of 1835.

Engine sides, painted on mahogany, usually cost the fire company from $300 to $1,000. The subject matter was usually allegorical, or patriotic. A characteristic aspect of American "folk art" that attracts a wider circle of appreciation with each passing year, these engine sides form an important part of the Collection.

Paintings on Parade

Says I, "My dearest Sally, oh, Sally for your sake
I'll go to Californy and try to raise a stake."
Says she to me—"Joe Bowers, oh, you are the boy to win—
Give me a kiss to seal the bargain." And she threw a dozen in.

Along the sidewalks of New York, popular songs such as "Joe Bowers" echoed as tens of thousands thronged Broadway on October 17th, 1851. It was the Third Triennial Parade of the New York Fire Department.

The scene was described next day in the New York Herald: "*About twelve o'clock the jam on Broadway was at its densest . . . the national colors floating from hotels and public buildings added to the fete-day appearance of the city.*"

The preparations for the parade were recounted in the same newspaper: "*Engines had been burnished up, repainted, regilded, and decorated, without regard to expense. Hose-carts and hook-and-ladder trucks had been put in their best and neatest-looking condition . . . New uniforms had been ordered, the red shirts that had seen service and that had lost their brightness were laid aside for everyday use, and others of unexceptionable gloss and texture procured.*"

The Historical Collection perpetuates the memories of these gala parade days in many vestiges. For instance, the painted engine sides of New York's Lexington Engine Company which were proudly displayed in the 1851 procession are now in The Historical Collection. But let a reporter of that day describe the Lexington boys,

60 strong, as they marched down Broadway: "*The Lexington engine is of the Philadelphia style of build, double deck, fore and aft. Her body is of a bright vermilion color. The top of the box is an enamelled lake color. She is rivetted and studded with highly polished brass throughout. The footboards are the same lake color as the box. The levers are of polished steel. On the condenser case of the gallery, is a representation of the SPIRIT OF '76, entitled TIDINGS FROM LEXINGTON, most appropriate to her name; and on the other the BATTLE OF LEXINGTON.*"

FIRE ENGINE PANELS

1Q • AETNA No. 16. Volunteer Fire Company of New York City. By Thomas Sully, 1832.

2Q • LEXINGTON. Lexington Hand Pump Fire Engine, New York. Subject "Tidings from Lexington." By unknown artist, 1849.

3Q • LEXINGTON. Lexington Hand Pump Fire Engine, New York. Subject "Battle of Lexington." By unknown artist, 1849. (*Illustrated*).

4Q • AMERICUS. Americus Company No. 6, New York City. Subject "Translation of Psyche." By John A. Woodside, 1849. (*Illustrated*).

5Q • AMERICUS. Americus Company No. 6, New York City. Subject "Birth of Venus." By John A. Woodside, 1849.

6Q • HOPE. Hope Hose & Fire Engine Company. Subject "Hope." By John A. Woodside, 1835.

7Q • FRANKLIN. Franklin Engine Company, Philadelphia. Subject "Franklin." By unknown artist, 1830.

8Q • FRANKLIN. Franklin Engine Company, Philadelphia. Subject "Franklin and Kite." By unknown artist, 1830. (*Illustrated*).

9Q • FRANKLIN. Franklin Engine Company, Philadelphia. Subject "Franklin with Loaf of Bread." By David R. Etter, 1830.

10Q • FRANKLIN. Franklin Engine Company, Philadelphia. Subject "Franklin at Desk." By David R. Etter, 1830.

11Q • ROBERT MORRIS. Robert Morris Hose Company, Philadelphia. By unknown artist, 1830.

12Q • WECCACOE. Weccacoe Fire Engine Company. Subject "Mermaid and Her Lover." By John A. Woodside, 1840.

13Q • WASHINGTON. Washington Engine Company. Subject "Washington at Battle of Trenton." By John A. Woodside, 1853. (*Frontispiece*).

14Q • EAGLE. Eagle Fire Engine Company. Eagle Volunteer Company of New York. Organized 1831. By unknown artist, 1835.

15Q • EAGLE. Eagle Fire Engine Company. By unknown artist, 1835.

16Q • FAME. Fame Fire Engine Company of Phila. Subject "Lady with Guitar." By John A. Woodside, 1837.

17Q • FAME. Fame Fire Engine Company of Phila. Subject "Lady with Harp." By John A. Woodside, 1837.

18Q • UNION. Union Hose Company of Phila. By unknown artist, 1835.

19Q • UNION. Union Hose Company of Phila. By unknown artist, 1835.

20Q • WHITE ANGEL. White Angel Fire Company. Salem, Mass. By unknown artist, 1830.

21Q • Volunteer Fire Engine Company. Subject "Piquot Indians." By unknown artist, 1835.

22Q • Volunteer Fire Engine Company. Subject "Piquot Indians." By unknown artist, 1835.

23Q • LAFAYETTE. Lafayette Hose Company, Philadelphia, (small iron panel). By Thomas Sully, 1833. (*Illustrated*).

Like most historical representations of Benjamin Franklin's kite experiment, this engine side, painted about 1830 by an unknown artist, erroneously shows Franklin's son as a boy. Actually he was 21 years of age at the time. Panel belonged to Franklin Engine Company, of Philadelphia.

In 1833, Thomas Sully, one of the greatest 19th Century American artists, painted a likeness of the Marquis de Lafayette on this iron panel for the Lafayette Hose Company, of Philadelphia.

This was one of four patriotic panels owned by the Lexington Engine Company No. 7, established at New York City in 1849. The artist is unknown. The Lexington machine was a Philadelphia double-deck type, with steel end levers, and brass studs throughout.

Trophy, made of coin silver, presented to Robert Tempest, president of the Hibernia Fire Engine Co., of Philadelphia, by his fellow members "as a token of their high regard as a fireman and presiding officer." Dated February 20th, 1851.

"OH! Noble looks the Fireman   *An axe he carries by his side*
As dressed in black and red   *A helmet on his head*
He pushes proudly through the crowd   *And thus he goes to fight a foe*
With gay and cheerful tread;   *Most powerful and dread."*

When Good Fellows Get Together

THESE words from a fireman's song, published at Cincinnati in 1866, echoed through the flag-draped halls, lighted with Chinese lanterns, on those gala evenings when firemen exchanged honors and hospitalities.

It was the custom for engine companies to pay one another calls. When "visiting firemen" arrived at the depot of a neighboring city, there was usually a brass band on hand to greet them and a dinner afterwards at which oratory would accompany the presentation of a trophy to the guests.

Illustrated on the opposite page is a pitcher presented to one Robert Tempest by the members of the Hibernia Company. This Philadelphia company, instituted in 1752, went on an excursion in 1858 that covered New York City, Brooklyn, Boston, Charlestown, Mass., and Newark, N. J. Dressed in their regalia, which included red shirts, white gloves, white leather belts and their distinctive green hats and capes, the Philadelphians engaged in exhibitions and contests, torch-light parades, receptions with fire-works and sumptuous banquets.

At these dinners eight courses were not uncommon, with toasts proposed to "Our Army and Navy," to "The Field Cable," and even to "The Atlantic Ocean." On these occasions, say the records, "jokes and songs followed one after the other, and the company kept the mirth and joy flowing till a late hour, when they separated."

In these days of Auld Lang Syne, gifts between companies were exchanged, or, as frequently happened, an individual was honored with a trophy for service and valor.

Many of these silver trophies, reminiscent of the pleasant fellowships of fire-fighting, may be seen in The Historical Collection today.

FIREMEN'S TROPHIES

1R • PITCHER (Coin Silver by Krider, Philadelphia Silversmith). 1851. Presented to Robert Tempest, President of the Hibernia Fire Engine Company No. 1, by his fellow members as a token of their high regard as a Fireman and Presiding Officer. (*Illustrated*).

2R • SILVER TROPHY (Plated). 1880. Presented to The Association of Exempt Firemen of Paterson, N. J. by Liberty Fire Company No. 5 of Reading, Pa. (*Illustrated*).

3R • SILVER TROPHY (Plated). 1881. L. A. Pinget Prize Cup won by team of Engine Company No. 5, on the Target Excursion of Engine Companies Nos. 1, 2, 3 and 5 to New Brunswick.

4R • SILVER WATER PITCHER (Plated). 1875. Used by The Association of Exempt Firemen of Paterson, N. J.

5R • SILVER WATER PITCHER AND MUG ON STAND (Plated). 1885. Presented to Washington Engine Company No. 3 of Paterson, N. J. by Young America Hose Company No. 6 of Poughkeepsie, N. Y.

6R • SILVER WATER PITCHER AND MUG ON STAND (Plated). 1880. Used by The Association of Exempt Firemen of Paterson, N. J.

7R • LOVING CUP (Solid Silver). 1864. Presented to a member of the United States Fire Company for valiant service.

Many trophies were embellished with miniature examples of the fireman's equipment. This trophy, presented to the Association of Exempt Firemen, of Paterson, N. J. by Liberty Fire Company No. 5, of Reading, Pennsylvania is an example of the many trophies exchanged between companies of different communities.

J. Rieger Jr.

Painting of a hand-drawn steam fire engine model, considered one of the finest in North America's Collection. The original engine belonged to the United States Fire Company, of Philadelphia. It was in use about 1858.

The Age of Steam

*T*HE beginning of the 19th Century saw the genesis of the Age of Steam. John Fitch, Oliver Evans, James Watt, and George Stephenson in this country and in Great Britain contributed to the harnessing of engines to the power generated from the pressure of mere vapor. The steam boat and the locomotive had become well established before the steam fire engine made its widespread appearance in the 1850's. Ericsson and Braithwaite had built a steam fire engine as early as 1829, but all attempts to introduce this type of machine met with popular opposition.

The first city in the United States to adopt steam fire engines wholeheartedly was Cincinnati, Ohio, and, subsequently, one of its citizens, Alexander B. Latta, pioneered the movement by making several of these engines for companies in cities along the eastern seaboard.

The early steam fire engines were drawn by hand but, with the rise of the paid fire department system, horses supplanted manpower. And, of course, in the 20th Century horses bowed to motor-drawn fire apparatus.

Even when the coming of the "steamer" was inevitable, the old volunteer firemen clung desperately to the hand-pumper. This attachment for the hand-pumper found its parallel on the sea at this time where men with sails vied with steam vessels. Just as many clippers outran the steamboats of the era, an 1855 contest at City Hall Park in New York City between one of Latta's steamers and the "Hay-Wagon," a powerful hand engine, ended in a close decision favoring the latter. Yet, the relentless stamina of the steam fire engine was realized and firemen who witnessed the event knew that "steam was here to stay." A new epoch in fire-fighting had already begun. On land and sea, the Age of Steam was getting into full swing.

1S • ALARM STEAM ENGINE. Hand-made, horse-drawn for three horses. 1872.

2S • BROOKLYN, N. Y. No. 2. Hand-made, hand-drawn. 1856.

3S • BROOKLYN STEAMER. Experimental type copper used on top instead of iron. Made at the Clapp & Jones Plant, Hudson, N. Y. 1870.

4S • CATARACT STEAM FIRE ENGINE. Hand-made, hand-drawn. 1856.

5S • COLUMBIA STEAMER. Hand-made, hand-drawn. 1860.

6S • DEARBORN STEAMER. Hand-drawn, steam pumper. 1855.

7S • DEADVILLE STEAMER. Hand-made, hand-drawn. 1865.

8S • DEFENDER OF RICHMOND, VA. Hand-drawn. 1858.

9S • DEFENDER STEAMER. Hand-drawn. 1860.

10S • EAGLE COMPANY No. 1, Pittsburgh. Hand-made, hand-drawn. James Nelson. 1855.

11S • EAGLE STEAM ENGINE. Hand-drawn steamer by Silsby. Large boiler, wooden wheels, eagle on compression chamber. 1856.

12S • ELIZABETH, N. J. STEAMER. Horse-drawn, working model. 1880.

13S • EXCELSIOR. Hand-made, hand-drawn. The original of this model was used in New York City 1856-1862. 1858.

14S • EXEMPT OF PATERSON, N. J. Hand-made, hand-drawn. 1856.

15S • FAME HOSE COMPANY OF PHILADELPHIA, PA. Hand-drawn. 1858.

16S • FAME, Philadelphia, Pa. Hand-made, hand-drawn. 1856.

17S • FRANKLIN FIRE COMPANY. Hand-made, hand-drawn. 1855.

18S • FRANKLIN STEAMER. Horse-drawn. All metal model. 1853.

19S • FIRE DEPARTMENT No. 4 OF NEW YORK. Small automotive working model. 1904.

20S • HOPE STEAMER. Hand-made, hand-drawn. 1856.

21S • HOPE STEAM ENGINE. Hand-made, hand-drawn. 1856.

22S • JOE ROSS STEAMER. Horse-drawn, working-model. Three-wheeled engine by A. B. Latta of Cincinnati, Ohio. 1852.

23S • HOWARD STEAM ENGINE. Hand-made, hand-drawn, used in New York. Circa 1860. (*Illustrated*).

24S • LATTA STEAM ENGINE. Horse-drawn. Unique model, mounted upon three wheels. Model of Latta's second steam engine. 1853. (*Illustrated*).

25S • LINCOLN STEAMER. Hand-made, hand-drawn. 1867.

26S • MANHATTAN STEAMER. Hand-made, hand-drawn. Built by Lee and Larned. 1853.

27S • MELVILLE, MASS. STEAM ENGINE. Hand-made, hand-drawn. 1850.

28S • MAZEPPA No. 1. Hand-made, hand-drawn. 1856.

29S • NEPTUNE STEAMER. Hand-made, horse-drawn, designed by John Shoemaker, built by Silsby. 1856.

30S • NEW YORK STEAMER. Hand-made, horse-drawn. Brass model. 1860.

31S • OIL CITY STEAMER. Hand-drawn. 1865.

32S • PHILADELPHIA STEAMER. Hand-made, hand-drawn. 1860.

33S • PHILADELPHIA STEAM ENGINE. Hand-made, hand-drawn with snake mouth steam exhaust. 1856.

34S • PHOENIX. Hand-made, hand-drawn. 1860.

35S • PHOENIX ENGINE COMPANY, Philadelphia. Hand-made, hand-drawn. 1865.

36S • QUINCY STEAMER. Hand-made, hand-drawn. 1856.

Hand drawn steam engine, circa 1860, of the Howard Company No. 34, of New York City, organized in 1807. Familiarly known as the "Red Rover," this company's great rival was Constitution Company No. 29, known as "The Rooster."

37S • RESCUE STEAM ENGINE No. 3. Hand-drawn. 1856.

38S • SIOUX STEAMER. Hand-made, hand-drawn. Built by Amoskeag Manufacturing Company, of Manchester, N. H. 1859.

39S • STEAM FIRE ENGINE. Hand-made, hand-drawn. 1853.

40S • STEAM FIRE ENGINE. Hand-drawn. Built by Robert Toland, Catasaqua, Pa. 1853.

41S • STEAM FIRE ENGINE. Hand-made, hand-drawn. Won many prizes for workmanship. 1865.

42S • STEAM FIRE ENGINE. Hand-made, hand-drawn. 1860.

43S • STEAM ENGINE. Hand-made, hand-drawn with vertical boiler. Made for N. Currier, the famous lithographer, whose prints of fires and fire engines are celebrated. 1856.

44S • STEAM FIRE ENGINE. Hand-made, glass model. 1853.

45S • STEAM FIRE ENGINE. Hand-made model of one of first horse-drawn steam fire engines. Circa 1875.

46S • STEAM FIRE PUMPER. Glass model of a Silsby, hand-drawn engine (gooseneck). Built in Seneca Falls, N. Y. 1855.

47S • THE GEYSER. Hand-made, hand-drawn. 1860.

Although John Ericsson tried to introduce steam fire engines in the 1840's, it was not until the late 1850's, after Cincinnati adopted Latta's steamers, that American firemen utilized steam instead of muscle-power. By the 1880's horse-drawn steamers had replaced hand-drawn types. This steamer was painted in the 1870's, and signed R. Sayer.

48S • THE NEPTUNE. Hand-made, hand-drawn, rotary engine with horizontal boiler. The great amount of tubular heating surface permitted its prompt use. 1855.

49S • UNION COMPANY NO. 1. Hand-made, hand-drawn. 1856.

50S • U. S. FIRE COMPANY OF PHILADELPHIA. Hand-made, hand-drawn. Exceptional workmanship. 1858. (*Illustrated*).

51S • WATERBURY. Hand-made, hand-drawn. 1856.

52S • WATERVILLE, N. Y. Horse-drawn. Built by A. S. Bullard. 1876.

53S • WEEDEN STEAM ENGINE. Hand-made, hand-drawn, experimental upright. 1858.

FULL SIZE STEAM ENGINE

54S • HARMONY FIRE COMPANY OF PHILADELPHIA. Built for this old volunteer company, founded in 1784, this engine is a product of the Silsby Manufacturing Company, Seneca Falls, N. Y. It was one of the first steam fire engines in Philadelphia and was considered the most efficient and modern apparatus of its time. Because of its weight and the time required to operate it, it was shortly replaced by the more powerful horse-drawn type. Circa 1870.

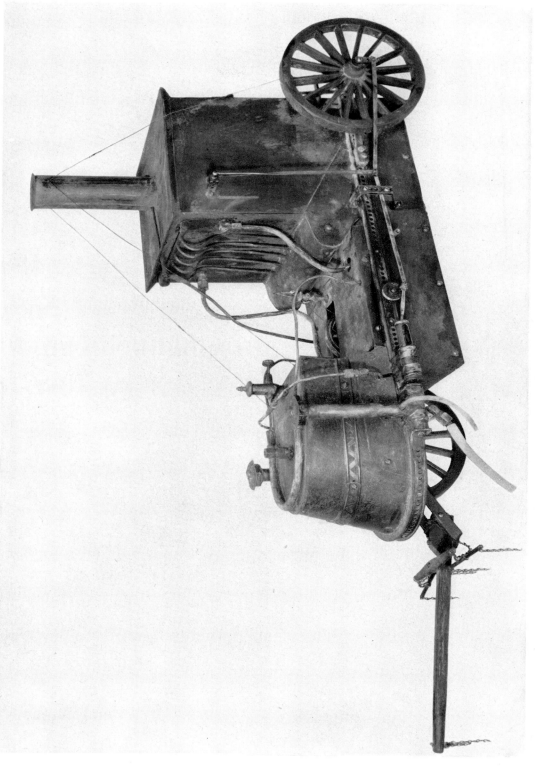

One of North America's rarest models is this 1853 three-wheel horse-drawn model of a steam fire engine, the work of A. B. Latta, of Cincinnati, Ohio, whose machines pioneered in changing U. S. fire-fighting methods. This is model of Latta's second fire steamer.

"Boiler on wheels," a hand-drawn steam fire engine, shows two engine plates, the pride of Philadelphia's Hope Company.
This engine was made by Reaney, Neafie & Co. who also built ships.

Men and Machines

WHY did the fireman regard his engine so highly? Many tales have been written about the keen affection felt by the volunteer firemen of yesteryear for their engines. Perhaps the explanation lies in the fact that the engine itself offered a common concern and pride which held the company members together as a ship holds together the members of its crew.

Take, for example, the Southwark Hose Company, whose engine plate is among the plates of old time engines in The Historical Collection. Located at 2nd and South Streets in Philadelphia, this company included many prominent men who had volunteered in the War of 1812 as the "First Independent Company of Artillerists." In 1820, they purchased a hose carriage, built by Jeffries & Nuthall at a cost of $397.

Since this represented a sizeable outlay, we can well imagine the care and attention given to this apparatus by those patriotic fire-fighters. In 1822, they constructed a torch for its front and, in 1823, upon having the carriage repainted in blue, one of the members, the celebrated American portrait artist, John Neagle, volunteered to decorate it. Youthful and fervent, these volunteers were held together by the ardent responsibility of keeping their machine in excellent running order. Among Neagle's fellow-volunteers were Archibald Randall, later a Federal judge, Thomas S. Bell, afterwards a Justice of the Pennsylvania Supreme Court, and Wilson Jewell, who became a prominent physician.

The "masheen" provided experiences that drew together men from every walk of life. Moreover, each company's apparatus was an individual piece of craftsmanship; old time volunteers swear that these machines were as high-spirited and capricious as thoroughbred horses. So highly were these well-beloved machines held that, even after they were no longer useful, their engine plates were kept in engine-houses as remembrances.   Many of these plates, recalling machines and those who manned them, have an honored place in The Historical Collection.

ENGINE   PLATES   (Metal)

1T • American LaFrance Fire Engine Company, Elmira, N. Y. 1870.

2T • Amoskeag Steam Fire Engine Company, Manchester, N. H. 1868.

3T • Columbia Hose Company, Philadelphia. 1806.

4T • Delaware Fire Company. 1761.

5T • Diligent Fire Company. 1791.

6T • Diligent Fire Company, Paterson, N. J. 1865.

7T • Director. 1875.

8T • Eagle Fire Company. 1850.

9T • Eagle Hook and Ladder Company No. 1. 1838.

10T • Edward Leverich. 1868.

11T • Elias Thayer. 1838.

12T • Engineer. No date.

13T • Engineer, Fire Department No. 3. 1850.

14T • Franklin Fire Company No. 1, Chester, Pa. 1845.

15T • Franklin Fire Company, New York. 1838.

16T • Fairmount Fire Company No. 20. 1823.

17T • Good Will Fire Company, Philadelphia, Pa. 1802.

18T • Good Intent Hose Company, Philadelphia. 1804.

19T • Hibernia Hose Company. 1823.

20T • Hibernia Hose Company. 1823.

21T • Hope Hose Company, Philadelphia. 1805.

22T • Hunneman & Company, Boston, Mass. 1872.

23T • Hudson Hose Company, New York. 1840.

24T • Hayes Fire Truck, Chelsea, Mass. 1835.

25T • Independence Fire Company. 1840.

26T • L.F.D. from Union Company of Lancaster, Pa. 1850.

27T • Liberty Fire Company No. 1. 1860.

28T • Liberty Hook and Ladder Company No. 16. 1840.

29T • Massachusetts Fire Company, Chelsea, Mass. 1835.

30T • Mechanics Hook and Ladder Company. 1850.

31T • Mechanic Hose Company. 1839.

32T • Northern Liberty Fire Company. 1756. (Illustrated).

33T • Northern Liberty Hose Company. 1828.

34T • Northern Liberty Hose Company. 1828.

35T • Newton No. 3. 1850.

36T • Phoenix Fire Company. 1808.

37T • Phoenix Fire Company. 1810.

38T • Roswell Flower No. 3. 1870.

39T • Stephen Thayer. 1838.

40T • U. S. Hose Company. 1808.

41T • Valley Forge. 1820. (Illustrated).

42T • Valley Forge. 1820.

43T • Vigilant. 1825.

44T • Vigilant No. 2, Paterson, N. J. 1840.

45T • Vigilant No. 6, Paterson, N. J.

46T • Volunteer Fire Company. No date.

47T • Waterford. No date.

48T • Weccacoe Fire Company. 1800.

49T • Unidentified. 1800.

50T • Unidentified. 1830.

Old-time fire laddies prized the name plates of engines as seamen valued the stern ornaments and figure-heads of vessels. Engine plates were made of metal, usually brass, and were kept brightly polished. The Northern Liberty Company, established in 1756, in Philadelphia, prided itself on its machines. Among its members was Richard Mason, pioneer fire engine builder, whose machines were known all over America and in the West Indies.

19th Century penchant for lush decoration manifested itself in invitations to balls and cards of thanks issued by fire companies. Shown here is a card thanking a military-aid committee for refreshments when the Fairmount Company helped to stem a blaze in 1863 at the Philadelphia Navy Yard.

North, East, South, West

WHEN the Insurance Company of North America was founded at Independence Hall, George Washington was serving his first term as president of the United States. It was 1792, a year that saw the 15th state, Kentucky, added to the field of stars on the American flag. There were only six cities, (Philadelphia, Boston, Charleston, New York, Baltimore, and Salem) with populations of eight thousand or more, and the great natural resources of America were as yet undeveloped. Then, as now, there were prophets of doom for America's future. Yet for those who had vision— then as now—the future offered a challenge that was to be met by enterprise and responsibility.

This faith in America is recalled by the many aspects of the nation's development which are represented in The Historical Collection. Here are milestones of America's march across the continent; no geographical boundaries limit the national character and scope of these treasures. The Historical Collection, ranging widely in time and area, tells a story of pioneers in every decade at every point on the American compass.

There is, for example, a large variety of fire-fighting material gathered from many sources. There are weathervanes from old fire-houses; certificates and scrolls—gems of the printmaker's craft—from fire companies as far apart as South Carolina and California; old photographs of volunteers, fire houses, and fire engines.

In The Collection, many unusual tools and pieces of equipment add to the story of volunteer days. There are, for example, eighty-nine fire axes, fifty-eight segments of leather hose, and forty-three tar-pots which once swung from the axles of the hand-drawn machines. There are six exceptionally rare flambeaux which once were used to light the way for nocturnal fire-fighting missions of the firemen of yore. And there are twenty-seven bed-keys which firemen employed to unlock beds in order to save these articles of furniture in days when their sections were locked by bolts.

There are one hundred and sixty-one hat-front shields of leather and metal; these shields, bearing numerals and emblems, were used as identification. Many of these are ornate and picturesque examples of the coveted presentation type that volunteers gave to men who had won their esteem.

Eighty-two engine lamps, twenty-six hand lamps, and one hundred and twenty-two torches recall the days when streets and roads after nightfall were illumined, if at all, by the light of the moon. The engine lamps in this group contain many handsome and fancy specimens since most firemen spared no costs in order to decorate their carriages with silver-plated and brass lamps, emblazoned with the company name and number. Some of the hand lamps and torches were carried in torch light parades which were held on special occasions.

Many extraordinary types of play pipes and hose nozzles remain as relics of bygone hand pumpers and hose carts. The simple method of waking the neighborhood to the danger of fire is shown by a large variety of rattles. Made of wood, these rattles are capable of a loud and distinctive noise-making. The Collection also includes fire salvage bags. Once a commonplace possession in Colonial households, the salvage bags are now great rarities. These bags were thrown to the street upon the sound of rattles and the outcry of fire. Firemen, picking up the bags, employed them to carry valuables from burning buildings.

FIRE TOOLS AND MEMORABILIA

1U • ARM BANDS (Leather). (6)*

2U • AXES. (89).

3U • AXE HOLDERS. (6).

4U • BATONS. (2).

5U • BED KEYS. (27).

6U • BOXES. Alarm (1). Ballot (5). Tool (1). (7).

*Indicates Quantity of Each Item.

7U • BRASS STATUE OF FIREMAN. (3).

8U • BUCKLER. (9).

9U • CHAIN FIRE ESCAPE. (3).

10U • CHEMICAL FIRE EXTINGUISHERS. (2).

11U • CHINA STATUE OF FIREMAN. (1).

12U • CHINESE FIRE-FIGHTING SUIT. (1).

13U • DOOR STOP. Marble. (1).

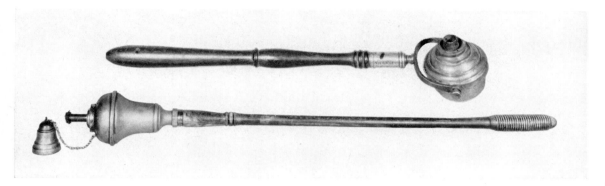

In the dead of night, runners to the fire lighted the way with oil lamps carried by handles. During nocturnal parades, these torches, carried by firemen, added a picturesque note to the spectacle.

14U • DOOR OPENER. Leather Corded. (1).

15U • ENGINE HOUSE KEYS. (4).

16U • ENGINE HOUSE LOCKS. (3).

17U • ENGINE HOUSE LAMP AND HOLDER. (1).

18U • ENGINE JACKS. (36). (*Illustrated*).

19U • ENGINE PULLER (Leather Straps). (2).

20U • FIRE ENGINE BELLS. (18).

21U • FIRE ENGINE DECORATION (Eagle on Staff). (1).

22U • FIRE GUN. (1).

23U • FIRE HOSE CHOKE. (1).

24U • FIRE HOSE COUPLING. (14).

25U • FIRE HOSE HOLDERS. (10).

26U • FIRE MASK. (1).

27U • FIRE HOSE, NOZZLE, AND COUPLING. (1).

28U • FIRE HOSE SECTIONS. Leather. (58).

29U • FIREMEN'S BADGES. (223).

30U • FIREMAN'S CANE. (1).

31U • FIREMEN'S HOOKS. (2).

32U • FIREMEN'S SHIRTS (Red Flannel). (2).

33U • FLAMBEAUX (Torches). (6). (*Illustrated*).

34U • GREASE, OR TAR, POTS. (43).

35U • HAND SPRINKLER. (1).

36U • HAND SQUIRTS (Wooden and Pewter). (8).

37U • HAT FRONT SHIELDS. (161).

38U • HOT TODDY OR LEATHER BLACK JACKS. (4).

39U • HYDRANT COVERS. (2).

40U • LAMPS (Engine). (82). (*Illustrated*).

41U • LAMPS (Hand). (26).

42U • MEDALS 1800, 1859, 1865, 1876. (4).

43U • MEGAPHONES. (8).

44U • MODEL OF OLD PUMP. (1).

45U • MUGS (Shaving and Beer). (2).

46U • NOZZLES (Fire Hose). (77).

47U • OIL CAN WITH CHAIN. (1).

48U • PANEL, carved wood from Hose Wagon 1865. (1).

49U • PANEL, wooden with painted head of tiger. (1).

50U • PANEL, wooden with motto "We Lend a Hand." (1).

51U • PITCHERS (China). Wedgwood (Chicago Fire Scene). Franklin Fire Company of Chester. Hanley Fire Company of Chester (2). Moyamensing Hook & Ladder Company. (5).

52U • PLAY PIPES. (18).

53U • POTTERY (Staffordshire) Statue of Fireman. (2).

When engine wheels came off, as happened
frequently on unpaved streets of early days, the
axle was hoisted by a jack. The jack shown
here belonged to Philadelphia's Fame Company, which went out of existence in 1823.

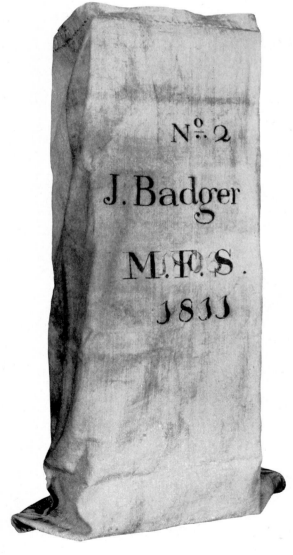

A rare collector's item: this salvage bag, dated 1811, is
typical of the kind householders used even prior to the
Revolution. Salvage bags, made of linen, were used in
order to gather up valuables in case of fire.

54U • RATTLES (Alarm and Watchman). (95).

55U • ROOF AND DOOR OPENER. (2).

56U • SALVAGE BAGS. (5). (*Illustrated*).

57U • SPANNERS. (92).

58U • SPANNER AND WRENCH COMBINATION. (34).

59U • SPIKE TORCH. (2).

60U • TORCHES. (122).

61U • WRENCHES. (32).

62U • WRENCH AND PICK COMBINATION. (1).

63U • WOODEN WATER MAIN SECTIONS. (41).

64U • WEATHERVANE. Hook and Ladder. 1830. (2).

65U • WEATHERVANE. Hand Pump Engine taken from engine house of an old volunteer fire company. 1845.

66U • WEATHERVANE. Philadelphia Hose Reel, used on top of Star Hose Company Engine House. 1840.

67U • WEATHERVANE. Hand Pump Fire Engine.

68U • WEATHERVANE. Hook and Ladder taken from top of volunteer fire house. 1853.

By the 1840's, lamps on fire engines were heavy and ornamented, usually made of brass, or silver-plated. Company names were ground into the glass. Above: a signal lamp of the Essex Company, Salem, Massachusetts.

127

70U • CHARLES SHAFFER. Certificate of membership in Phoenix Hook and Ladder Company. 1878.

71U • CHARLESTON, S. C. Certificate of Membership. 1823.

72U • CALIFORNIA VETERANS. Certificate of Membership. 1877.

73U • CITY OF BROOKLYN, N. Y. Certificate of Membership to Frank Melio.

74U • CITY OF NEW YORK. Certificate of Membership. 1799.

75U • DANVERS FIRE COMPANY. Certificate of Membership. 1832.

76U • DECATUR FIRE COMPANY. Certificate of Membership to John E. Schlafer, Frankford, Phila. 1871.

77U • DAVID M. LYLE, Chief of Phila. paid Municipal Fire Dept. Memorial Certificate.

78U • DILIGENT HOSE COMPANY. Certificate of Membership to J. M. Hopper. 1871.

79U • ENGINE COMPANY No. 14. City of Boston, Mass. 1858.

80U • FRIENDSHIP FIRE COMPANY No. 3, of Baltimore, Md., instituted 1785.

81U • GOOD - WILL FIRE COMPANY. Certificate. 1857. (Illustrated).

82U • HAND-IN-HAND. Certificate. 1878.

83U • HAND-IN-HAND FIRE COMPANY. Boston, Mass. Certificate.

84U • HARMONY COMPANY, Trenton, N. J. Certificate of Membership to A. Smith. 1871.

85U • HOPE HOSE COMPANY, Philadelphia. Certificate of Membership to James Barnard. (Duval and Hunter). 1871.

86U • HUMANE FIRE COMPANY No. 13, Phila. Certificate of Membership. 1868.

87U • JOHN MARKAUN. Certificate, Association for Relief of Disabled Firemen, Philadelphia. 1864.

88U • JOHN NICHOLS. City of New York Certificate. 1829.

89U • NEW YORK FIRE DEPT. Original Certificate of Membership (Currier & Ives). 1832.

90U • NEW YORK FIRE DEPARTMENT. Certificate of Membership. 1829.

91U • NEW YORK FIRE DEPARTMENT. Fireman's Membership Certificate. 1829.

92U • NEPTUNE HOSE COMPANY. Philadelphia. 1865.

93U • PATERSON FIRE ASSOCIATION. Volunteer Fireman's Certificate. 1789.

94U • PENNSYLVANIA FIRE COMPANY. Fireman's Membership Certificate. 1871.

95U • PHILADELPHIA FIRE COMPANY. Fireman's Membership Certificate. 1871.

96U • RESOLUTION FIRE COMPANY. New York Certificate. 1829.

97U • ROBERT STERLING. Jersey City, N. J. Certificate. 1865.

98U • SAMUEL THOMPSON. New York City, Certificate. 1829.

99U • SAN FRANCISCO FIRE DEPT. Certificate of Membership. 1856.

100U • U. S. HOSE COMPANY. To George A. Hicks. Certificate. 1858.

101U • VOLUNTEER FIREMEN OF CITY OF NEW ORLEANS. Membership Certificate. 1871.

102U • VETERAN FIREMEN'S ASSOCIATION OF CALIFORNIA. Certificate. 1877.

103U • VETERAN FIREMEN'S ASSOCIATION OF PHILA. To Hugh Hatton for honorary service with Globe Fire Company. 1887.

104U • WILLIAM PENN HOSE AND STEAM FIRE COMPANY No. 18 OF PHILA. To J. E. Staniford Company. Motto "Like William Penn we will be useful to our fellowmen." (Max Rosenthal).

105U • HOPE HOSE COMPANY No. 6, Newton, Mass. To W. H. Aylers, Jr., Newton, Mass. Fire Dept. 1868.

Certificates of membership were adorned with scenes of fires and sometimes engraved with allegorical subjects. This Trenton, New Jersey certificate of the Good Will Company is typical of many issued in the last century.

PHOTOGRAPHS

106U • ANNUAL CONVENTION NATIONAL ASSOCIATION OF FIRE ENGINEERS. Philadelphia. 1876.

107U • BARNICOAT FIRE ASSOCIATION. Visiting Philadelphia. 1903.

108U • CATARACT HOSE REEL IN FRONT OF FIRE HOUSE. Paterson, N. J.

109U • CHARLESTOWN, MASS. Hand Pump Engine Company, assembled for parade. 1880.

110U • DELEGATES' ANNUAL MEETING. Delaware Engine Company. 1848-1849.

111U • EAGLE HOOK AND LADDER. Paterson, N. J. 1870.

112U • ENGINE HOUSE No. 10. Charlestown, Mass. 1835.

113U • EAGLE COMPANY No. 3. Boston, Mass. showing engine and company in front of fire house. 1800.

114U • FAME HOSE COMPANY. 1840.

115U • FAIRMOUNT HOSE COMPANY. No. 32, Philadelphia. 1823.

116U • FIREMEN'S ASSOCIATION OF NEW YORK. Excursion to State Volunteer Firemen's Convention. 1899.

117U • FIREMEN'S PROCESSION. Union Square, New York City. 1858.

118U • "PASSING WASHINGTON MONUMENT."

119U • FIREMEN IN FRONT OF CITY HALL. Philadelphia. 1885.

120U • HORSE-DRAWN FIRE ENGINE. Early type 1858.

121U • HAND DRAWN, HAND PUMP FIRE ENGINE. Used in Philadelphia. 1790.

122U • HAND PUMPER. City of Somerville Veterans.

123U • HAND DRAWN HAND PUMPER. As used in vicinity of Long Island City. 1794.

124U • HAND PUMP FIRE ENGINE. Pacific Fire Company. 1885.

125U • HAND-IN-HAND STEAM FIRE ENGINE COMPANY. Trenton, N. J. 1860.

126U • HUMANE No. 1. FIRE COMPANY. Norristown, Pa. in front of Fire House. 1852.

127U • LIBERTY No. 7, STEAM ENGINE. 1872.

128U • MASSACHUSETTS HOOK AND LADDER COMPANY No. 1. 1850.

129U • MEMBERS OF THE U. S. FIRE ENGINE COMPANY. Philadelphia, Pa. 1850.

130U • MEMBERS OF THE CHARLESTOWN, MASS. VETERANS. 1850.

131U • NEPTUNE FIRE COMPANY.

132U • NORTHERN LIBERTIES FIRE COMPANY No. 1. 1828.

133U • OFFICERS OF THE PHILADELPHIA FIRE DEPARTMENT. 1870.

134U • OVATION OF WELCOME TO FIRE ZOUAVES. 1870.

135U • RECEPTION OF 29TH REGIMENT AT PHILADELPHIA. 1893.

136U • SALEM HAND PUMPER IN FRONT OF CUSTOM HOUSE. Boston, Mass. 1790.

137U • U. S. HOSE COMPANY & FAME HOSE COMPANY. Philadelphia, Pa. 1840.

138U • VETERAN VOLUNTEER'S FIRE ENGINE. In front of fire house. 1845.

139U • VETERANS' HAND PUMPER. Philadelphia. 1840.

140U • VETERAN FIREMEN'S ENGINE HOUSE. Philadelphia, Pa. 1850.

141U • VETERAN FIREMEN OF BOSTON, MASS. Hand Pumper. 1835.

142U • VETERAN VOLUNTEER FIREMEN'S HISTORICAL ASSOCIATION OF LOUISVILLE, KY. In front of fire house. 1905.

143U • VETERAN FIREMEN'S ASSOCIATION OF PHILADELPHIA. In front of City Hall on departure for Boston, Mass. 1897.

144U • VETERAN FIREMEN'S ASSOCIATION. 1870.

145U • VOLUNTEER FIREMEN OF PHILADELPHIA. On steps of Union League before starting for New Orleans. 1888.

146U • VOLUNTEER FIREMEN'S ASSOCIATION OF PHILADELPHIA.

147U • WASHINGTON FIRE ENGINE COMPANY, Philadelphia. 1870.

148U • WATERFORD, N. Y. STEAM PUMPER. Horse-drawn, built by L. Button and Son.

149U • WELCOME TO VISITING FIREMEN. Showing two Steam Pumpers and Hose Carriage.

MISCELLANEOUS

150U • PRESENTATION SHIELD. Ridgewood Association to Vigilant Fire Company No. 6 of Paterson, N. J.

151U • SHEET OF STATIONERY, showing Engine House of U. S. Firemen.

152U • SHEET OF MUSIC of Trojan Hook and Ladder Company No. 3. 1857.

153U • SHEET MUSIC "Centennial Quick Step." 1876.

154U • Songs of American Firemen.

155U • STOCK CERTIFICATE to William Powell for ten shares of Capital Stock in Insurance Company of North America. 1799.

156U • The Birth of Agency System in America. (2). 1807.

157U • TRIBUTE by South Penn Steam Forcing Company No. 37, Philadelphia, at death of Abraham Lincoln.

THE AMERICAN FIREMAN.
Always Ready

Mr. Nathaniel Currier, himself a fireman, posed for this 1858 Currier & Ives print "Always Ready," one of a set of four colored lithographs entitled "The American Fireman." Issued in the last century at $1.25 each, this group of prints has climbed to handsome prices because of value as collector's items.

Mr. Currier as a Fireman

IN 1884, the print-making house of Currier & Ives, 115 Nassau Street, New York City, issued a catalogue of "Celebrated Fire Pictures." These prints sold at prices of $3.00 and $1.25. Not a few of these came to grace the walls of the Insurance Company of North America.

In recent years, the value of these prints has soared. Collector's items today, they frequently sell at prices in three figures. Currier & Ives prints have come to be recognized as unique historical records in addition to having a pictorial charm that makes them vibrate with the movement of America's growing days.

Nathaniel Currier, born at Roxbury, Massachusetts, opened his first New York shop at 1 Wall Street in 1835. In 1857, his name became coupled with that of his general manager, James Merritt Ives, who was born at New York City in a small house on the grounds of the Bellevue Hospital (his father was superintendent of the famed hospital). The firm of Currier & Ives hired a number of artists for its staff, and issued lithographic prints of various sizes, although the usual size was 9 by 12 inches. In a period when newspapers and most magazines lacked pictures, these colorful prints were extremely popular.

Among the most favored prints issued by Currier & Ives were those dealing with fires. Currier, aware of the dramatic impact of the New York fire of 1835, published one of the first great fire prints. In later years, when any city suffered a major conflagration, he was quick to create a print depicting the blaze at its most furious aspect.

Mr. Harry Peters in his definitive work, "Currier & Ives, Printmakers to the American People," states that the fire-fighting engines were drawn from the original, and that the firemen's faces were portraits.

Indeed, in the print "Always Ready," it was Mr. Currier himself who posed for the artist.

Prints of Fire Pioneers

Only a few prints illustrating how people lived or worked in America were published in the 18th Century. It was not until after 1818, when Bass Otis made the first lithographs in America, that scenes of American life found a ready market.

Public imagination was stirred as America, after its first hardy labors, halted to look at itself on paper and in ink. There were colorful scenes printed of military victories, natural wonders (such as Niagara Falls), and the new bridges that spanned the nation's rivers. There were pictures of paddle-wheel steamboat races, and fast packet-vessels, and buffalo hunts in the West. The print-makers, establishing shops in many cities, hired artists to depict the growing nation in action.

One of the first print-makers to realize the popularity of prints relating to fires and firemen, as told on the preceding page, was Nathaniel Currier. His instant success in this field opened business opportunities for lithographers and engravers who, likewise, began to publish prints treating with fires, firemen and their engines.

Among the prints in The Historical Collection are several with the rare imprint of George H. Heiss, who was a specialist in producing lithographs of fire engines. Another print-maker, considered by many as having an equal footing in craftsmanship with Currier & Ives, was the French-born Peter S. Duval; he is represented by a rare print that was once given by the Hibernia firemen of Philadelphia to the Washington Fire Company No. 5 of Charlestown, Massachusetts.

In this large group of prints, the pictorial history of fire-fighting in America is presented. Here are scenes of great fires in New York, Philadelphia, Cincinnati, San Francisco, Pittsburgh, and other cities. Here, too, are the celebrated engines— the first in Brooklyn, and Troy, N. Y., and Engine No. 5 of Worcester, Mass.—and many other well-beloved old "masheens."

In the print-makers of the nation, the volunteers had eloquent spokesmen to

As the foreman exhorts the volunteers pulling the White Turtle of the Northern Liberty Company to outstrip the Red Crab of the Lafayette Hose Company, a familiar scene of the 1840's is captured for all time in this old print, made in Philadelphia.

tell the story of their calling. During the era of the hand-drawn apparatus and volunteer firemen, photography was in its infancy and photo-engraving was unborn. It is the print-maker who delineated this adventuresome era, enabling us to visualize it in full sweep.

White Turtle vs. Red Crab

On this page, the *White Turtle*, a hose carriage of the Northern Liberty Company, is racing the *Red Crab*, of the Lafayette Hose Company. The scene is in Philadelphia during the tempestuous days of rivalry when each company maintained watches in cupolas and towers in order to be first in sounding an alarm and reaching the fire.

The membership of the volunteer fire company was usually recruited from the neighborhood in which the fire-house was located. Many companies were formed of tradespeople and merchants; for example, in New Orleans, the Mechanics No. 6 was

135

organized in the 1830's among employees of Jedediah Leeds' foundry—hence, the name of the company.

The fire company house was indeed something of a club for the volunteers. The boys would gather round the open fire on winter nights and listen to old-timers tell of blazes vanquished only by herculean efforts. On summer nights, the firemen would spend a pleasant evening, beguiling the time with close harmony when an itinerant street fiddler, or barrel-organ operator, came their way. They devised songs about their own good fellowship, and composed derisive doggerel about their rivals.

In these fire-houses, many mementos were saved. Thus, The Historical Collection has been enriched through the old fire-houses, which, in truth, were the first museums of fire-fighting material. In these old fire engine houses, life was full of good fellowship and while the quarters sometimes were ruffled by pranks and the practical jokes of rivals, they offered a social life and a strong bond of camaraderie.

In fact, one newspaper of the 1850's, in describing the handsome and comfortable house of a New York engine company, noted that "the room is ventilated by two large windows at each end, and surmounted by a large skylight; and a fine flower garden is in the rear of the building. Many a fireman would rather spend his days in such quarters than in his own home."

CURRIER AND IVES LITHOGRAPHS

1V-3V • BURNING OF CRYSTAL PALACE, New York, 1854.

4V • THE NIGHT ALARM—"*Start Her Lively Boys.*" 1854. Life of a Fireman Series (*Illustrated*).

5V-8V • THE RACE—"*Jump Her Boys, Jump Her.*" 1854. Life of a Fireman Series.

9V • THE FIRE—"*Now Then With a Will, Shake Her Up Boys.*" 1854. Life of a Fireman Series.

10V • THE RUINS—"*Take Up—Man Your Ropes.*" 1854. Life of a Fireman Series. (*Illustrated*).

11V-12V • THE NEW ERA—"*Steam and Muscle.*" 1854. Life of a Fireman Series.

13V-19V • THE METROPOLITAN SYSTEM, 1854. Life of a Fireman Series.

20V-31V • LIFE OF A FIREMAN, 1854. Series of six lithographs. Originally issued at $3.00 each. 26 x 36 inches.

32V • PRAIRIE FIRES OF THE GREAT WEST.

33V-35V • BOSTON FIRE OF 1872.

36V-41V • CHICAGO FIRE OF 1871.

42V • DILIGENT FIRE ENGINE. Dated 1845. Type of engine used from 1791 to 1831. The company was founded in 1791.

43V • THE GREAT FIRE OF 1835, New York City. "The Fire."

44V • HIBERNIA ENGINE HOUSE.

THE LIFE OF A FIREMAN.

Louis Maurer, of Currier & Ives, who drew "The Life of A Fireman" series, regarded this group as the finest work in his career. In addition to being an artist, he was a renowned dead-shot, having taught marksmanship at Palisades Park, N. J. during the Civil War. He was a warm friend of Wm. F. (Buffalo Bill) Cody.

45V-46V • FACING THE ENEMY, 1858. The American Fireman Series.

47V-48V • PROMPT TO THE RESCUE, 1858. The American Fireman Series.

49V-50V • RUSHING TO THE CONFLICT, 1858. The American Fireman Series.

51V-52V • ALWAYS READY, 1858. The American Fireman Series. (*Illustrated*).

53V-54V • THE AMERICAN FIREMAN, 1858. The American Fireman Series of four lithographs. Originally issued at $5.00 for entire set.

55V • THE PRIZE SQUIRT, 1889. The Darktown Fire Brigade Series.

56V-59V • THE LAST SHAKE, 1889. The Darktown Fire Brigade Series.

60V • GOING TO THE FIRE, 1889. The Darktown Fire Brigade Series.

61V-62V • TO THE RESCUE, 1889. The Darktown Fire Brigade Series.

63V-64V • ALL ON YOUR METTLE, 1889. The Darktown Fire Brigade Series.

65V • SLIGHTLY DEMORALIZED, 1889. The Darktown Fire Brigade Series.

66V • HOOK AND LADDER GYMNASTICS, 1889. The Darktown Fire Brigade Series.

67V • SAVED, 1889. The Darktown Fire Brigade Series.

68V-69V • TAKING A REST, 1889. The Darktown Fire Brigade Series.

70V-71V • INVESTIGATING A SMOKE, 1889. The Darktown Fire Brigade Series.

72V-83V • DARKTOWN FIRE BRIGADE, 1889.

THE LIFE OF A FIREMAN.

A documentary print, lithographed by N. Currier (the firm name in 1854 when this print was issued), shows various types of apparatus in service, a fire hydrant, riveted hose, and foreman with trumpet. Note firemen coupling hose with spanners. This print was colored by hand.

Model of hose cart used by artists staff of Currier & Ives for fire drawings is in North America's Collection. Artists at Currier & Ives often collaborated on a single delineation; one artist worked on figures, another on background, while a third transferred the sketch to lithographing stone.

84V-85V • AMOSKEAG FIRE ENGINE, 1860. Print of steam fire engine of Amoskeag Company, Manchester, N. H.

86V • AQUATONE, 1859. Hand Pump Fire Engine.

87V • AMERICAN HOSE COMPANY, 1859. Lithograph.

88V • AMERICAN STEAM FIRE ENGINE. Early type engine.

89V • A LIGHT STEAM FIRE ENGINE, 1860. Built by Lee and Larned.

90V • BOOKLOVERS LIBRARY FIRE, 1860. Showing fire damage.

91V • BOSTON ENGINE NO. 5, of Worcester, Mass. Lithograph.

92V • BURNING OF ASSEMBLY BUILDING, 1851. Gleason's Drawing Room Print.

93V • BURNING OF UNION LEAGUE. Philadelphia, Penna.

94V • CASCO HAND PUMP ENGINE, Portland, Me., 1852.

95V • CATARACT HOSE COMPANY, Paterson, N. J., 1885. Fire House and Hose Wagon.

96V • CATARACT HOSE COMPANY, Paterson, N. J., 1830. Hose reel in front of Fire House.

97V • CATARACT HOSE COMPANY, Paterson, N. J., 1885. Hose Reel.

98V • CHARLESTOWN, MASS. HAND PUMP ENGINE. Early 19th Century.

99V • CHARLESTOWN, MASS. ENGINE COMPANY NO. 10. Engine House.

100V • CHEMICAL ENGINE, 1880. Horse drawn engine.

101V-102V • CINCINNATI FIRE, 1878. Print.

103V • EXCHANGE BUILDING FIRE, New York City, 1834.

104V • EXPLOSION AND RESULTING FIRE, New York City, 1850.

105V • FAIRMOUNT HOSE COMPANY, No. 32.

106V • FIRE ENGINES—12 TYPES, 1883. Showing historical development from 1568 to 1882, by Sackett & Wilhelms.

107V • FIRE, New York City, 1835.

108V • FIRE SCENE, 1835. Showing ruins of New York City Fire.

109V-110V • FIRE, New York City, 1835.

111V • FIRE, Philadelphia Business District, 1900.

112V • FIRE, Philadelphia, 1903.

113V • FIRE ENGINE NO. 38. New York Engine.

114V • FIRE CHIEF AND COMPANY. Perseverance Hose Company.

115V-116V • FIREMEN'S PARADE, 1880. Print showing firemen passing City Hall, Philadelphia.

117V-120V • FIREMEN PAST AND PRESENT.

121V • FIREMEN OF VARIOUS NATIONALITIES.

122V • FIREMEN'S PROCESSION, 1858. Showing parade passing Cooper Union Square, New York.

123V • FIRE ENGINE AND FIRE ESCAPE. Showing early types used in Birmingham, England.

124V • FIRST NEW YORK FIRE ENGINE, 1730 type.

125V • FIRST BROOKLYN FIRE ENGINE, 1785 type.

126V • FOREIGN SQUIRT BRIGADE.

127V • FOR LIFE OR DEATH, 1874. Print, silk woven, of Fire Engine. T. Stevens.

128V • FRANKLIN ENGINE COMPANY NO. 3. Brooklyn, N. Y. Company.

129V • GASPEE FIRE ENGINE, 1835. Providence, R. I.

130V-131V • GRAND ERIE CANAL CELEBRATION. Parade in celebration of opening of Erie Canal, 1820.

132V • GOOD INTENT FIRE COMPANY, 1819.

133V • GUARDIAN FIRE COMPANY.

134V • HAND PUMPER OF BAW BESSE COMPANY, 1881. South Gardiner, Mass.

135V • HAND PUMP FIRE ENGINE. Print of oldest hand-carried hand pumper in America. Original built in England in 1698.

136V • HAND PUMP FIRE ENGINE. Engine built by Patrick Lyon.

137V • HAND PUMP FIRE ENGINE. Engine used from 1750 to 1860.

138V • HAND PUMP FIRE ENGINE. Hand-drawn engine owned by Steam Fire Engine Company of Trenton, N. J.

139V • HENRY A. COOK, Vice-President of Hibernia Company, Philadelphia.

140V • HIBERNIA ENGINE COMPANY, Philadelphia, 1858.

141V • HIBERNIA HAND PUMPER, 1835. Showing Pumper in Parade.

142V • HIBERNIA HOSE REEL NO. 2.

143V • HOPE HOSE COMPANY. Showing company at Crystal Palace, New York City.

144V • INTERNATIONAL EXHIBIT, 1876, Philadelphia. Print of Fire Apparatus built by Silsby & Co., Seneca Falls, N. Y.

145V • "IS THIS 1935?" 19th Century Fantasy, horse-drawn fire engine.

146V • LAFAYETTE STEAM FIRE ENGINE COMPANY NO. 8, 1872.

147V • LONDON FIRE BRIGADE.

148V • LIBERTY FIRE ENGINE NO. 7. Engine in front of fire house.

149V • LONDON FIRE-FIGHTING APPARATUS, early type.

150V • MECHANIC HOSE REEL NO. 2, Brooklyn, N. Y., 1857.

151V • MEMBERS OF LONDON FIRE COMPANY ESCORTING PRINCE OF WALES, 1860.

152V • NEPTUNE STEAM FIRE ENGINE, Philadelphia. Earliest type of steam fire engine.

153V • NEW YORK FIRE DEPARTMENT, 127 Mercer Street, N. Y. C.

154V • NEW YORK FIRE ENGINE COMPANY'S HAND PUMPER, 1730. Small hand pump fire engine.

155V • NEW YORK HOSE COMPANY.

156V • NEW YORK FIREMEN'S MONUMENT IN GREENWOOD CEMETERY.

157V • NEW YORK FIRE INSURANCE PATROL, 1876.

158V-159V • NONANTON, MASS. FIRE ASSOCIATION.

160V • NORTHERN LIBERTY NO. 16 FIRE COMPANY. Hand-drawn hose reel.

161V • OLYMPIC THEATRE FIRE, 1874. Print on tin.

162V • OUR FIRE LADDIES, 1892.

163V • OSWEGO, NEW YORK FIRE, 1850.

164V • PARADE BY GAS LIGHT. Broadway, New York City.

165V • PARISH FIRE ENGINE.

166V • PENNSYLVANIA FIREMEN OF 1840.

167V • PHILADELPHIA HAND PUMPER.

168V-169V • PHILADELPHIA FIRE DEPARTMENT PARADE, 1865.

170V-172V • PHILADELPHIA FIRE DEPARTMENT OF 1850.

173V • PHILADELPHIA FIRE DEPARTMENT AT DEDICATION CEREMONIES, Washington National Monument, 1854.

174V • PHILADELPHIA HOSE COMPANY HOUSE, 1835.

175V • PHILADELPHIA VETERAN FIREMEN.

176V • PHOENIX FIRE ENGINE NO. 22.

177V-178V • PITTSBURGH FIRE. Fire of April 10, 1865.

179V • PHILADELPHIA FIRST FIRE INSURANCE PATROL.

180V • RELIANCE HAND PUMP FIRE ENGINE COMPANY. Company founded 1786.

181V • RUNNING TO THE FIRE, 1858. Harrison and Weightman.

182V • RUNNING TO THE FIRE, 1870.

183V • SALEM, MASS. HAND PUMPER.

184V-185V • SAN FRANCISCO FIRE, 1906.

186V • SILSBY ROTARY FIRE ENGINE, 1876. Print from Scientific American.

187V • SILSBY FIRE ENGINE, 1848. Print of Engine including Holby's Patent Pump.

188V • SILSBY ENGINE DEVELOPMENT, 1865.

The Conflagration of the MASONIC HALL, Chesnut Street, Philadelphia,
which occurred on the Night of the 9th of March 1819.

Not far from Independence Hall, this 1819 fire caused an outpouring of engine and hose companies. All the figures are in the
vivid, robust style of John Lewis Krimmel (1787-1821), known as "the American Hogarth." The plate is by Hill, noted
American engraver.

189V • SILSBY & COMPANY STEAMER, 1858.

190V • SILSBY & COMPANY DISPLAY OF APPARATUS.

191V • STEAM FIRE ENGINE, 1865. Hand-drawn engine built by Julius Runge.

192V • STEAM FIRE ENGINE. Horse-drawn engine built by L. Button & Son of Waterford, N. Y.

193V • STEAM FIRE ENGINE STARTING FOR FIRE, 1860.

194V • SOMERVILLE HAND PUMPER.

195V • STEAM ENGINE OF BALTIMORE FIRE COMPANY. Sketch of engine with specifications.

196V • SCENES OF METROPOLITAN FIRE DEPARTMENT, 1866.

197V • SCENES BEFORE AND AFTER GREAT FIRE OF PITTSBURGH, 1845.

198V • THE BOY VOLUNTEER.

199V • THE LATE FIREMEN'S ANNUAL PARADE IN NEW YORK CITY, 1853.

200V • THE NEW STEAM FIRE ENGINE, 1856. Print from Scientific American.

201V • THE WHITE TURTLE AND THE RED CRAB. Race between two fire companies, Philadelphia. Circa 1840. (*Illustrated*).

202V • THE VETERAN'S FIRE ASSOCIATION.

203V • UNITED STATES FIRE COMPANY, 1811.

204V-207V • UNITED STATES FIREMEN. Engine House of Eagle Volunteer Company No. 2 organized in New York in 1831.

208V • UNION FIRE ENGINE COMPANY OF SALEM, MASS. "Oldest Fire Engine in United States."

209V • VARIOUS TYPES OF FIRE ENGINES, 19th Century.

210V • VETERAN'S STEAM PUMPER, 1835. Hand-drawn pumper.

211V • VETERAN'S HAND PUMPER IN FRONT OF CITY HALL, Toronto, Canada.

212V • VETERAN FIREMEN'S ASSOCIATION, City Hall, Philadelphia, 1880.

213V • VETERAN VOLUNTEER FIREMEN'S ENGINE, Brooklyn, N. Y.

214V • VIGILANT NO. 6 OF PATERSON, N. J., 1845. Button type hand pumper.

215V • VOLUNTEER FIREMEN OF MIDDLESEX, MASS.

216V • VOLUNTEER FIREMEN'S DEMONSTRATION, 1900.

217V • VOLUNTEER FIREMEN'S ASSN. OF NEW YORK CITY.

218V-219V • WASHINGTON ENGINE COMPANY NO. 3 STEAM ENGINE. Hand-drawn engine, Paterson, N. J.

220V • GEORGE WASHINGTON HELPING TO EXTINGUISH A FIRE.

221V • WARREN ENGINE NO. 4. Charlestown, Mass. Engine.

222V • WECCACOE HOSE COMPANY HOSE WAGON, Philadelphia.

223V • WECCACOE FIRE COMPANY HAND PUMPER.

224V • YANKEE HAND PUMPER NO. 5. Boston, Mass.

225V • ASSISTANCE FIRE ENGINE HOUSE, 1884. Lithograph showing engine house on Crown Street, Philadelphia.

226V-228V • BURNING OF MASONIC HALL, Chestnut Street, Philadelphia, 1819. Engraving by J. Hill, Artists: J. L. Krimmel and S. Jones. (*Illustrated*).

229V • CHIEF LYLE. First Chief of Philadelphia Paid Fire Dept.

230V • CHICAGO FIRE OF 1871. Lithograph by Charles Graham.

231V • COOPER VOLUNTEER REFRESHMENT SALOON, Philadelphia, 1862. Lithograph.

232V • DILIGENT FIRE ENGINE. Engine used from 1791-1831.

233V • DILIGENT FIRE ENGINE, dated 1844. Lithograph of hand-drawn hand-pumper from original built by Patrick Lyon in 1820 and rebuilt by J. Agnew, 1836, by George Heiss, Philadelphia.

234V • EARLY FIRE SCENE, "*Many Happy Days.*"

235V • FAIRMOUNT FIRE COMPANY HAND PUMPER, Philadelphia, dated 1855. Lithograph by George Heiss, Philadelphia.

236V-241V • GREAT ENGINE CONTEST OF OLD PHILADELPHIA FIRE DEPARTMENT, 1850. Lithograph showing scene at 5th and Market Streets, July 7, 1850, by C. H. Spieler.

242V-243V • HAND PUMP FIRE ENGINE. Lithograph of hand-drawn engine built by Hunneman & Company, Boston, Mass.

244V • HIBERNIA ENGINE COMPANY NO. 1 OF PHILADELPHIA. Assembling for Parade October 5th, 1857. "Presented by Hibernia Company No. 1 to Washington Fire Company No. 5 of Charlestown, Mass. in remembrance of Old Lang Syne." Lithograph by Duval. Presentation copy.

245V • HIBERNIA ENGINE COMPANY NO. 1 OF PHILADELPHIA. Assembling for parade in front of Hibernia Fire House. Lithograph by Duval.

246V • HIBERNIA ENGINE COMPANY NO. 1 OF PHILADELPHIA. Lithograph showing President of Company, Robert Tempest, and Vice President John Barton. Company founded 1752. Lithograph by Scott and Martin.

247V • HIBERNIA ENGINE. Lithograph of engine built by John Agnew.

248V • HIBERNIA HAND PUMPER AND MEMBERS OF COMPANY. Lithograph showing company in parade dress.

249V • HOPE HOSE COMPANY OF PHILADELPHIA. Lithograph by George Heiss, Philadelphia.

250V • HOPE HOSE STEAM FIRE ENGINE NO. 2, Philadelphia. Lithograph by George Heiss, Philadelphia.

251V • HOPE HOSE COMPANY NO. 4, Philadelphia. Company in front of fire house. Lithograph by George Heiss, Philadelphia.

252V • PANORAMA OF AMERICA'S GREAT FIRES. Lithograph depicting fires at: San Francisco, Calif., 1857. Portland, Me., 1866. Chicago, Ill., 1871. Boston, Mass., 1872 (Iroquois Theatre). Ottawa, Can., 1900. Paterson, N. J., 1902. Chicago, Ill., 1903. Rochester, N. Y., 1903.

Baltimore, Md., 1904. Pittsburgh, Pa., 1897. Jacksonville, Fla., 1901.

253V • PENNSYLVANIA HALL FIRE. Philadelphia. Engraving by John Sartain.

254V • PHILADELPHIA HOSE COMPANY STEAM FIRE ENGINE. Lithograph by George Heiss, 1858.

255V • PHILADELPHIA VOLUNTEER FIREMEN'S ASSOCIATION.

256V • PHILADELPHIA FIRE DEPARTMENT REFRESHMENT SALOON, 1850.

257V • PARLIAMENT BUILDING FIRE HOUSE OF LORDS AND COMMONS. Lithograph 1834 from original drawing by Wm. Heath made on stone by light of the flames. Graff & Soret.

258V • REUBEN HAINES, originator of Hose Company of Philadelphia. Albert Newsam.

259V • REPRESENTATION DE FEU TERRIBLE A NOUVELLE YORCK. Description in French and German. Francois Haberman.

260V • STEAM FIRE ENGINE. All parts of engine marked.

261V • STEAM FIRE ENGINE. Lithograph. Specifications and Drawings of Engine by A. Cherreveau, 1857.

262V • STEAMER "JERSEY" ON FIRE IN DELAWARE RIVER. Lithograph, showing list of saved, missing, and dead. 1856.

263V • THREE PENNSYLVANIA FIREMEN IN REGULATION DRESS, 1840.

264V • TROY, N. Y. FIRST FIRE ENGINE, 1798.

265V • WASHINGTON ENGINE NO. 5. Lithograph of Charlestown, Mass. Engine.

266V • WEBSTER NO. 13 HOSE CARRIAGE AND FIRE ENGINE, 1835.

267V-268V • WEST PHILADELPHIA HOSE COMPANY STEAM FIRE ENGINE NO. 3, 1844. Lithograph by George Heiss, Philadelphia.

JOSEPH BALL • *Third President, January 1798 - July 1799* • *Director 1792 - 1803*

Painted by Gilbert Stuart, (1755-1828), the most famous of early American portrait artists. Stuart painted portraits of many of the celebrated artists of his day, including Benjamin West and Sir Joshua Reynolds. In 1794, Stuart came to Phila-delphia, then the capital of the nation, where he set up a studio and painted portraits of many persons prominent in business and political life. His portraits of Washington and Jefferson are widely reprinted.

The Presidents and Directors

THE portraits of the Presidents and Directors of the Insurance Company of North America are to be seen in the company's head office at 1600 Arch Street in Philadelphia.

In the story of the nation's rise, we find that the land was made great by men who met events with force of character and wisdom, and an abiding sense of public welfare. These qualities of leadership are found in the story of North America's growth and are manifest in the faces of the men whose portraits are in The North America Collection. The painting techniques of the artists vary widely but it is significant that each portrait is endowed with a solidity and power of conception in which one senses similar attributes among the men who have guided the Company's destiny.

One of the notable portraits on the Company's walls is that of Joseph Ball, 3rd president of North America, painted by Gilbert Stuart, the most celebrated portraitist of George Washington. Stuart, who came to Philadelphia in 1794, painted more than one hundred portraits of the nation's first Chief Executive.

Many of the portraits in North America's gallery were painted by men associated with The Pennsylvania Academy of the Fine Arts. John McLure Hamilton, Bernard Uhle, Hugh Breckenridge, Robert Vonnoh and Adolphe Borie are names linked with this famed institution, the oldest art school in America.

The portraits in The Historical Collection range in many styles of individualism, from the brilliant freshness and sparkle of the 18th Century style to the precision and

In North America's home office at Philadelphia, portraits of Presidents and Directors of the Company, ranging over a century and a half, lend historic association to the Board of Directors Room.

sturdiness of painting in the last century. In the latter style, Jared Bradley Flagg, born in 1820, who continued his art for many years after he became a minister in the Episcopal Church, painted George Leib Harrison, who served as a Director of the North America from 1854 to 1885.

Canvases by Adolphe Borie, Edmund C. Tarbell, and Nikol Shattenstein lend a 20th Century note to the array of distinguished paintings which includes many schools of art and many generations of portraitists. Ranging from the 18th Century to our own times, these paintings project the presences of men who built carefully and strongly. Here are personalities who saw the chronicle of America unfolding and, who, assuming responsibilities for their part in the nation's narrative, have given shape and form to North America's part in history.

PORTRAITS OF PRESIDENTS AND DIRECTORS

of Insurance Company of North America

1W • COLONEL CHARLES PETTIT. 2nd and 4th President, 1796-1798, 1799-1806. By unknown artist.

2W • JOSEPH BALL, 3rd President, 1798-1799. By Gilbert Stuart. (*Illustrated*).

3W • JOHN INSKEEP, 5th President, 1806-1831. By Nikol Shattenstein.

4W • JOHN CORREY SMITH, 6th President, 1831-1845. By Nikol Shattenstein.

5W • ARTHUR GILMAN COFFIN, 7th President. 1845-1878. By Samuel B. Waugh. (*Illustrated*).

6W • CHARLES PLATT, 8th President. 1878-1909. By Meyer Dantzig.

7W • CHARLES PLATT. 8th President. 1878-1909. By unknown artist.

8W • EUGENE L. ELLISON, 9th President, 1909-1916. By Hugh Breckenbridge.

9W • BENJAMIN RUSH, 10th President, 1916-1939. By Edmund C. Tarbell.

10W • BENJAMIN RUSH, 10th President. 1916-1939. By Adolphe Borie.

11W • JOHN OSGOOD PLATT, 11th President, 1939-1941. By John C. Johansen.

12W • JOHN A. DIEMAND, 12th President, 1941- By Nikol Shattenstein.

13W • SAMUEL W. JONES, Director, 1807-1873. By Samuel B. Waugh.

14W • SAMUEL F. SMITH, Director, 1830-1835, 1838-1862. By unknown artist.

15W • JOHN ALEXANDER BROWN, Director, 1828-1872. By Samuel B. Waugh.

16W • CHARLES TAYLOR, Director, 1836-1873. By Jared B. Flagg.

17W • AMBROSE WHITE, Director, 1839-1873. By Samuel B. Waugh.

18W • WILLIAM WELSH, Director, 1842-1878. By Samuel B. Waugh. (*Illustrated*).

19W • GEORGE LEIB HARRISON, Director, 1854-1885. By Jared B. Flagg.

20W • FRANCIS R. COPE, Director, 1855-1904. By Bernard Uhle.

21W • EDWIN S. CLARKE, Director, 1862-1898. By Bernard Uhle.

22W • THOMAS CHARLTON HENRY, Director, 1864-1890. By Bernard Uhle.

23W • EDWARD SWIFT BUCKLEY, Director, 1882-1910. By Hugh Breckenridge.

24W • JOHN STORY JENKS, Director, 1885-1923. By Alice M. Roberts.

25W • EDWARD H. COATES, Director, 1885-1921. By John McLure Hamilton. (*Illustrated*).

26W • GEORGE H. McFADDEN, Director, 1887-1922. By Hugh Breckenridge.

27W • EDWARD HOPKINSON, Director, 1887-1935. By Hugh Breckenridge.

28W • WILLIAM DAVIS WINSOR, Director, 1889-1917. By Robert W. Vonnoh.

29W • HENRY WILLIAMS BIDDLE, Director, 1891-1923. By Robert W. Vonnoh. (*Illustrated*).

30W • C. HARTMAN KUHN, Director, 1895-1940. By O. Merkel.

31W • CHARLES S. W. PACKARD, Director, 1901-1937. By Wm. M. Paxton.

32W • BAYARD HENRY, Director, 1904-1926. By Leopold Seyffert.

33W • EDWARD S. BUCKLEY, JR., Director, 1910-1943. By Lazar Raditz.

ARTHUR GILMAN COFFIN • *Seventh President, 1845 - 1878* • *Director, 1846 - 1881*

The portrait of Arthur Gilman Coffin is by Samuel B. Waugh (1814-1855), who, as a boy, studied under John Rubens Smith, teacher of Thomas Sully and Emanuel Leutze.

EDWARD HORNOR COATES • *Director 1885 - 1921*

The portrait of Edward Hornor Coates was painted by John McLure Hamilton, (1853-1936). His paintings are represented in many galleries in this country and England. Among them are portraits of Cardinal Manning and George Meredith, the novelist. Hamilton was a prominent member of the Royal Society of Portrait Painters and was considered in art circles abroad as one of America's most eminent portraitists.

WILLIAM WELSH • *Director 1842 - 1878*

Portrait by Samuel B. Waugh (1814-1885). Born at Mercer, Pa., this noted 19th Century portraitist began his career as an artist in Philadelphia, upon completion of studies in Italy, France, and England. His portrait of Abraham Lincoln is owned by The Pennsylvania Academy of the Fine Arts.

HENRY WILLIAMS BIDDLE · *Director 1891 - 1923*

The artist is Robert William Vonnoh, (1858-1933). Born at Hartford, Connecticut, he studied in Paris, taught in Boston and Philadelphia. Considered one of America's leading portraitists, examples of his work are to be found in the leading museums. His "Family of Woodrow Wilson" hangs in the White House.

THE INSURANCE COMPANY OF
NORTH AMERICA,

IN compliance with the wishes of many persons who have been in the habit of Insuring their property against Loss or Damage by Fire, and also with a view to encourage others to follow their laudable example, have Reduced their Premiums, to a rate, it is presumed, unexceptionably moderate. This is, therefore, to give notice to those who may choose to avail themselves of the means thus offered, to guard against the calamitous injuries too often sustained by Fire, that the Company will effect Insurance on every species of property, not only in the city of Philadelphia, but in other parts of the United States.

Letters of enquiry, as well as orders for Insurance remote from this city, will be promptly attended to, if addressed to

JOHN INSKEEP, President.

Insurance Office of North America, Philadelphia. June 4, 1808.   wstf

---

British Manufactures,

JUST RECEIVED,

Per the Jane, from London and the America, from Liverpool,

AND FOR SALE,

ON LIBERAL TERMS,
BY THE SUBSCRIBERS,
BY THE PACKAGE,
No. 39 north Front street,

CALICOES,
6-4 and 9-8 Ginghams,
India Chintz Furnitures,
9-8 and 7-8 Shirtings,
Dimities
6-4 Cambrics,
Fancy Muslins and Shawls,
Figured and plain British black Muslins,
6-4 Tamboured Laced Cambrics,
Fancy Figured Gauze Do.

GRAY & KENNEDY,

HAVING AGAIN COMMENCED

BREWING,

At No. 24 south Sixth-street,

RETURN thanks to their friends and public in general, for favors conferred last season, and hope that their attention to business will insure them further encouragement.
sept 17   eot

FOR SALE,

A LARGE vacant lot of ground, situate on the east side of Front near South street, containing in breadth twenty seven feet, and in depth 130 feet, extending to Penn street, clear of all incumbrance, being part of the estate of Patrick Linehan, deceased.

N. B. Any person desirous of purchasing the above lot will please apply to either of the subscribers.

Among the old historical papers in North America's Collection, this first advertisement of fire insurance in 1808 bears the familiar eagle emblem. Excerpt is from Poulson's Daily Advertiser, of Philadelphia.

Archives of Integrity

IT may be said that The Historical Collection has been built from material which connects the parallel growth of the Insurance Company of North America and the United States of America. In this chronicle of growth, the records of the past are preserved in many forms, not least among which are the early documents and books telling, in the language of business, the part played by the North America in national events.

Names that are celebrated in the annals of the nation's history may be found in these early archives of North America's business achievements: Robert Morris, the financial genius of the Revolutionary War; Stephen Girard, the most famous American merchant of his time (whose fortune founded Girard College); Thomas Fitzsimons, Irish-born signer of the U. S. Constitution; William Waln, one of the family whose ships helped in opening American trade with China.

Here, too, one finds the name of Thomas Mifflin, the quartermaster of Washington's army, who, as Governor of Pennsylvania, signed the North America's charter of incorporation. Another name is that of an attorney for North America, Joseph Hopkinson, who wrote the patriotic hymn "Hail Columbia" in 1798.

In the days of national crisis, in war and depression, these records tell of the stalwart action of men whose decisions added to the reputation and integrity of North America. In the pages of these priceless records of the Company's history, one discovers the quintessence of the American character and genius which have contributed so greatly to the advancement of the nation's present position in the world.

"The whole insurance machine exists for the protection of and service to the policyholder," said Mr. Benjamin Rush, Chairman of the Board of Directors, in 1939.

This fact becomes instantly salient when the history of insurance in the United States is reviewed.

Time changes methods, regulations, and fashions in business but principle is an unchanging and unshifting foundation stone upon which a business will abide successfully. The documents and letters in The Historical Collection of the North America bear testimony to the Company's principle of "protection of and service to the policyholder."

Here are the footnotes that serve to illuminate the history of North America as it marched with the nation in times of national crisis. In the fine script of quill pens on durable rag paper, the letters and papers of North America's formative days reveal the instinctive ability of principled men to protect the policy-holder.

There are also many documents that have been preserved for their unique historical association. For example, a letter from Benjamin Franklin in France, and a missive from General Washington from Trenton in 1776 written to Robert Morris. One of the outstanding items of the Collection is a marine policy insuring a ship at Marseilles written in Latin during the year 1584.

Many insurance policies of early days contribute to the wealth of historical value in North America's collection of documents. For instance, there is a fire insurance policy issued to Bushrod Washington on "Mount Vernon," the first president's home in Virginia.

EARLY RECORDS AND HISTORICAL DOCUMENTS

Including a Miscellany

1X • ACCOUNTS. 1838-1872.

2X • ACCOUNTS. Dec. 1876. Sept. 1877.

3X • CASH BOOK. 1801-1810.

4X • COMPANY REPORTS. 1793-1838.

5X • COMPANY REPORTS. 1800-1807.

6X • COMPANY REPORTS. 1818-1829.

7X • CONSTITUTION. Jan. 16, 1793.

8X • DIRECTORS' MINUTE BOOKS. Vol. 1, 1792-1803, Vol. 2, 1803-1812. Vol. 3, 1812-1825. Vol. 4. 1825-1845. Vol. 5, 1845-1860. Vol. 6, 1860-1876. Vol. 7. Vol. 8, 1887-1893. Vol. 9, 1893-1902.

Vol. 10, 1902-1912. Vol. 11, 1912-1919. Vol. 12, 1919-1925. Vol. 13, 1925-1927.

9X • DIVIDEND BOOK. 1810-1823.

10X • FIRE BLOTTER. No. 3, 1801-1805.

11X • FRENCH CLAIMS. 1797-1800.

12X • LETTER BOOK. 1802-1806.

13X • LETTER BOOK. 1806-1815.

14X • LETTER BOOK. 1815-1846.

15X • LETTER COPY BOOK. May-Nov. 1870.

16X • LOSS BOOK. Feb. 1849-July 1850.

17X • MARINE BLOTTER. C, Mar. 6, 1794 to June 3, 1794. D, June 1792 to Nov. 1794. E, Nov. 1794 to July 15, 1795. F, July 1795 to Feb. 1796.

18X • MARINE BLOTTER. 1799-1800.

19X • MARINE BLOTTER. 1802-1805.

20X • MARINE BLOTTER. 1805-1806.

21X • MARINE BLOTTER. 1806-1823.

22X • MARINE BLOTTER. 1817-1828.

23X • NORTH AMERICA LEDGER. 1793-1795.

24X • NORTH AMERICA LEDGER. 1807-1827.

25X • RECEIPT BOOK. 1798-1802.

26X • RECEIPT BOOK. 1802-1812.

27X • STOCKHOLDERS' MINUTE BOOK. 1803-1857.

28X • STOCKHOLDERS' MINUTE BOOK. 1858-1912.

29X • STOCK LEDGER. Dec. 1792 March 1796.

30X • $124,000,000 N. A. COMPANIES. Fortune Magazine. Feb. 1937.

31X • APPEAL, 1809. James Reed & William Poyntell for funds to support Engine Associations and Hose Companies.

32X • APPROVAL, 1794. To purchase 50 shares of stock in Pennsylvania Bank.

33X • APPLICATION, 1792. For position of clerk from William Henshaw.

34X • BILL, 1792. From John Fenno for publishing Constitution of North America.

35X • BILL, 1794. From John Fenno for printing and advertising.

36X • BILL, 1789. Benjamin Wilson for 2000 quills.

37X • BILL, 1792. Joshua Gilpin for foolscap paper.

38X • BILL, 1792. John and William Wigglesworth for sweeping, dusting and brushes.

39X • BILL, 1792. "Claypoole for advertising."

40X • BILL, 1798. For House Badges.

41X • BOOK, 1735. Dutch Prints.

42X • BOOK. Various paintings of Benjamin Franklin.

43X • COPY, 1792. Minutes of Universal Tontine Association.

44X • COPY, 1768. Pennsylvania Chronicle.

45X • DOCUMENT, 1792. Incorporation of Insurance Company of North America.

46X • PAPER, 1794. Dunlap and Claypoole "American Daily Advertiser."

47X • ENVELOPE, 1937. Contents carried on first air flight from China to United States, with cancelled stamp.

48X • FIRST CASH BOOK of Insurance Company of North America, 1792.

49X • FIRST LETTER BOOK of Insurance Company of North America, 1792.

50X • FIRST MINUTE BOOK of Insurance Company of North America, 1792.

51X • FIRST RECEIPT BOOK of Insurance Company of North America, 1793.

52X • GOLD PIECE. Salvaged from S. S. Egypt, sunk off France in 1922.

53X • LETTER, 1776. George Washington to Robert Morris from Camp Trenton.

54X • LETTER, 1785. Benjamin Franklin from Passy, France.

55X • LETTER, 1792. Ebenezer Hazard to John M. Nesbitt.

56X • LETTER, 1793. Ebenezer Hazard to John M. Nesbitt, during Yellow Fever Epidemic.

57X • LETTER, 1793. Ebenezer Hazard to Nathan Hazard.

Philadelphia

1792
Sitting Committee, Mess.rs McConnel & Ball.

Dec.r 15.th Policy N.o 1.
Wrote for Conyngham, Nesbitt & Co.
at & from Philadelphia to Londonderry
on the Ship America, James Ewing M.r
valued at Twelve Thousand Dollars
5.333.33 Doll.r @ 2¼ ℗ C.t ------- 120.—
Policy --- .— 50

Doll.s C.t
120. 50

Dec.r 15.th Policy N.o 2.
Wrote for Conyngham, Nesbitt & Co.
at & from Phil.a to Londonderry on Goods
on board the Ship America, James
Ewing Master
3200 Doll.s @ 2¼ ℗ C.t ------- 72.—
Policy — - - - .50

.. 72. 50

Dec.r 15.th Policy N.o 3.
Wrote for John Leamy at &
from Phil.a to New Orleans, with Liberty
to touch & trade at Cape Francois, on
Goods on board the Brig Margarita
Anthony Arnaud, Master
1500 Dollars @ 3 ℗ C.t ------ 45.—
Policy ——— - - .50

.. 45. 50

Dec.r 15.th Policy N.o 4.
Wrote for Stuart & Barr, (at &
from Alexandria in Virginia to
Falmouth in Great Britain, to trade
between Europe (without the Streights)
& America, for nine Months, com=
=mencing this Day, & to continue until
the Ships Arrival at any safe Port
in the United States, after the Expi=
=ration of the said nine months)
on the Ship Friendship, Samuel
Hubbel

58X • Letter, 1793. John M. Nesbitt to Ebenezer Hazard.

59X • Letter, 1793. Thomas Elder from "German Town" (Philadelphia).

60X • Letter, 1793. Nancy Viol requesting insurance on Brig "Mary."

61X • Letter, 1793. William Gordon telling of death of Marat.

62X • Letter, 1794. Benjamin Rush regarding rates on Brig "Betsy."

63X • Letter, 1797. Colonel Charles Pettit.

64X • Letter, 1799. Ebenezer Hazard to Col. Charles Pettit.

65X • Letter, 1799. Joseph Nicholson.

66X • Letter, 1799. Stephen Girard requesting insurance on Brig "Mercury."

67X • Letter, 1800. Vanderbilt & Hicks requesting fire insurance on groceries.

68X • Letter, 1808. Charles Ellis accepting agency of Insurance Company of North America.

69X • List, 1800. French Captures of American Vessels Prior to 1800.

70X • Order, 1794. Stephen Girard on Rud India Logwood.

71X • Observations on Fire Insurance. 1803.

72X • Opinion, 1806. Joseph Hopkinson relative to election of President.

73X • Opinion, 1802. Jared Ingersoll, Esq. respecting attachments.

74X • Opinion, 1794. Joseph Moylan, Esq. re: case of Cargo on Brig "Industry."

75X • Original List of Books, 1802. Issued by Company for keeping records. Waste Book and Black Book.

76X • Original Dividend Book, 1793.

77X • Original Draft of Committee appointed to consider extending insurance in other states of Union, 1807.

78X • Original Bills of Lading (Marine), 1752, 1850, 1936.

79X • Pamphlet, 1801. "An Act" Insurance Company of North America to incorporate subscribers of North America Company. 1801.

80X • Petition, 1792. J. Buisson to inspect vessels.

81X • Philadelphia Directory, 1794. Showing George Washington's name.

82X • Poulson's Daily Advertiser, 1808. First Fire Insurance Advertisement. (*Illustrated*).

83X • Register, 1794. First Fire and Marine Policies.

84X • Receipt, 1792. Signed by Ebenezer Hazard.

85X • Retaining and Trial Fee of Jared Ingersoll, Esq., 1799.

86X • Receipt, 1795. Jasper Moylan for Legal Aid.

87X • Report of Committee for extending insurance to all parts of the U. S. 1796.

88X • Recommendation, 1792. John Valentine as porter for Insurance Company of North America.

89X • Recommendation of Committee as to Table of Rates, 1794.

90X • Receipt, 1792, from Federal Gazette and Philadelphia Advertiser for subscription.

91X • Schedule, 1797. Marine Rates.

92X • Stock Certificate, 1824. American Philosophical Society, Phila.

93X • Survey, 1798. 42 King Street, Charleston, S. C.

94X • Seal of Confederacy (facsimile). Circa 1863.

95X • Articles of Founding of Diligent Fire Company, Philadelphia, 1791.

96X • Articles of Incorporation of Reliance Fire Company, 1786.

97X • Banner, Charlestown Veteran Firemen's Association from Philadelphia Veteran Firemen's Association, 1817.

98X • Birth of Agency System in America, 1807.

99X • Brooches (Pair) portraying an early Hose Reel and a Hand Pumper.

100X • Charter of Assistance Fire Company, 1789.

101X • Card of Thanks to Fairmount Steam Fire Company, 1863.

Marine policy written in 1793 by North America. At that time, privateers roamed the seas in quest of plunder, and every journey was a dangerous venture against unknown perils. Nevertheless, North America in that year sustained only two marine losses.

102X • CARD of Thanks to Friendship Fire Company, 1856.

103X • CARD of Thanks from Guardian Hose Company No. 29 to Engine Companies of Providence, Boston and Lowell, Mass.

104X • CERTIFICATE presented to Hugh Hatton for honorary service with Globe Fire Company, 1887.

105X • EMBROIDERED MAT "Hook & Ladder Company No. 9, Boston, Mass."

106X • FIRE INSURANCE POLICY issued to Bushrod Washington on Mt. Vernon, former home of George Washington. Fairfax County, 1803.

107X • FIRE INSURANCE POLICY issued to Bushrod Washington on brick barn, Mt. Vernon, 1804.

108X • FIRE INSURANCE POLICY issued to John Hall, Physician, on three story brick house, 31 Filbert Street, Philadelphia, 1793.

109X • FIRE INSURANCE POLICY on Household Furniture, 1809.

110X • FIRE INSURANCE POLICY to Michael Ritter, Germantown, 1812.

111X • FIRE INSURANCE POLICY of Mutual Assurance Company (Green Tree) Phila. 1784.

112X • FIRE INSURANCE POLICY to Capt. Anthony Cuthbert, issued by Mutual Assurance Company. (Green Tree). Phila., 1786.

113X • FIRE POLICY, Perpetual No. 1, to Nathaniel Gordon, 1845.

114X • FIRE POLICY, Perpetual No. 2, to Robert Irvine, 1845.

115X • FIRE INSURANCE POLICY on Scenery and Wardrobe of New Theatre, Phila., 1807.

116X • FIRE INSURANCE POLICY to John DuBarry on Merchandise, 1808.

117X • FIRE INSURANCE POLICY to Alexander Henry & Company on Brick House, 192 South Side of High Street, Phila., 1808.

118X • FIRE INSURANCE POLICY to William Frances, 1809.

119X • FIRE INSURANCE POLICY to Catherine Schrack, 1825.

120X • MARINE POLICY "Ship St. Ilary" (Marseilles) Oldest Marine Policy. Written in Latin, 1584.

121X • MARINE POLICY, 1755.

122X • MARINE POLICY to William Fisher, 1754.

123X • MARINE POLICY to Michael Gratz, London to Philadelphia, 1760.

124X • MARINE POLICY "Ship Sterling," 1765.

125X • MARINE POLICY to Walter Stewart insuring Brig "Mary Ann," 1793.

126X • MARINE POLICY to Philip Care on Schooner "Mary," 1793.

127X • MARINE POLICY insuring Schooner "Fair Lady," 1794.

128X • MARINE POLICY to Nathaniel Hubbard insuring Sloop "Nancy," 1794.

129X • MARINE POLICY to Alexander Davidson insuring Brig "Betsy," 1794.

130X • MARINE POLICY to Samuel Clarkson insuring Schooler "Friendship," 1794.

131X • MARINE POLICY to John Mifflin, Goods and Merchandise insuring Brig "Sally," 1795.

132X • MARINE POLICY to Dean Timmons and George Norton, 1784.

133X • MARINE POLICY to Higbee and Milner insuring Sloop "Little Jim," 1800.

134X • MARINE POLICY to John Leamy insuring Brig "Baron De Carondelet," 1793. (*Illustrated*).

135X • GOOD WILL RESOLUTION of Passaic Steam Fire Engine Company No. 1 of Paterson, N. J. to Firemen and Citizens of Providence, R. I., and Salem, Mass., 1880.

136X • INVITATION of American Hose Company No. 17, to "Red Stockings."

137X • IRON SHOW CARD of Olympic Theatre Fire, Philadelphia (Roll of firemen killed and wounded).

138X • LEATHER INSIGNIA "Exempt Firemen's Association of Long Island," 1890.

139X • LEATHER INSIGNIA "Presented to Newburyport, Mass. Veteran Firemen's Association," 1866.

140X • LEATHER ARM INSIGNIA "Resolution Fire Company."

141X • LEATHER ARM INSIGNIA "Columbia Hose Guards."

142X • INSIGNIA "Lafayette Hook and Ladder Company."

143X • THREE FRAMES OF PLAYING CARDS, all scenes of Firemen and Volunteer Firemen Activities.

144X • PASSPORT signed by George Washington, 1797.

145X • PERMIT FOR SURVEY OF DWELLINGS, to John Donaldson, Baltimore, Md., 1813.

146X • PERMIT. U. S. PATENT OFFICE 1812. To Jacob Perkins and Allan Pollack for model of fire engine. As far as is known, this is first patent on a fire engine in the United States. Bears signatures of James Madison, then President, and James Monroe, who became the 5th President.

Rare engraving by Carwitham, showing extremely early concept of Philadelphia's waterfront. Windmill at extreme left represented "Windmill Island," in Delaware River. Tallest steeple belongs to Christ Church; small steeple at left was early, abortive tower on Independence Hall. This is the 1764 view, published by Carington Bowles, of London, in one of its earliest impressions.

A Tradition and a Heritage

PHILADELPHIA, birthplace of liberty, has been the headquarters of the Insurance Company of North America since 1792.

In that year, Philadelphia was the third largest English-speaking city in the world. It was the political capital of the new nation as well as the foremost port and economic center. George Washington lived in the Presidential Mansion on High Street, now called Market Street. On this street, just a short distance from the residence of Washington, stood the first building to be insured by the North America against fire. Perhaps his youthful ambition to follow the sea caused Washington to stroll frequently to the Delaware River in order to look at the ships and cargoes, many of them insured by the North America.

The City of Brotherly Love was a fire-conscious city. William Penn, who lived in London during the Great Fire, laid out his city in a pattern calculated to reduce fire losses. Its dwellings were built of brick rather than of wood. Under the aegis of Benjamin Franklin, it pioneered in volunteer fire-fighting when the Union Company was formed in 1736. The first two successful fire insurance companies in the Colonies —the Philadelphia Contributionship and the Mutual Assurance Company— originated in Philadelphia.

Among these traditions, the Insurance Company of North America began its life. The Company's first office, 119 South Front Street, was located in a neighborhood associated with stirring national events: just around the corner, the United States Marine Corps was founded at Tun Tavern, and, within a short walk, stood Carpenters' Hall, where the first Continental Congress had met.

It is very natural that many volumes of history connected with Philadelphia and its personalities should be found among those assembled in The Historical Collection. And, as in the stories of other American communities, the services of the Insurance Company of North America are to be found written on many pages in the story of Philadelphia.

BOOKS ON PHILADELPHIA

1Y • ALEXANDER GRAYDON'S MEMOIRS OF A LIFE. 1811. By Alexander Graydon.

2Y • AN EXPLANATION OF THE MAP OF CITY & LIBERTIES OF PHILADELPHIA. 1774. By J. Reed.

3Y • ANNALS OF PHILADELPHIA. 1830. By J. F. Watson.

4Y • CASKET 1832. 1832. By S. C. Atkinson.

5Y • GAZETTEER WESTERN CONTINENT. 1798. By Jedidiah Morse, D.D.

6Y • HISTORY OF INSURANCE, PHILADELPHIA. 1888. By J. A. Fowler.

7Y • HISTORY OF PENNSYLVANIA HOSPITAL, 1751-1895. 1895. By T. G. Morton, M.D.

8Y • HISTORY OF PHILADELPHIA, Vol. 1-2-3. 1884. By Scharf & Westcott.

9Y • HISTORY OF PHILADELPHIA, 1812-1814. 1839. By D. Bowen.

10Y • LIFE OF WILLIAM PENN. 1852. By Samuel M. Janney.

11Y • MARKET STREET, PHILADELPHIA. 1918. By Joseph Jackson.

12Y • MEMOIRS OF DAVID RITTENHOUSE. 1813. By William Barton.

13Y • OLD ROADS OUT OF PHILADELPHIA. 1917. By J. T. Faris.

14Y • OUR FIRST CENTURY, 1776-1876. 1881. By R. M. Devens.

15Y • PHILADELPHIA & HER MERCHANTS. 1860. By A. Ritter.

16Y • PHILADELPHIA DIRECTORY. 1811. By James Robinson.

17Y • PHILADELPHIA DIRECTORY. 1838. Arranged by J. R. Savage.

18Y • PHILADELPHIA DIRECTORY. 1848. By Edwin C. & John Biddle.

19Y • PROUD'S HISTORY OF PENNSYLVANIA, Vol. 1, 1797; Vol. 2, 1798. By Robert Proud.

20Y • SALLY WISTER'S JOURNAL. 1902. By A. C. Myers.

21Y • STEPHEN GIRARD. 1832. By Stephen Simpson, Esq.

22Y • THE AUTOBIOGRAPHY OF BENJAMIN FRANKLIN. 1906. By Benjamin Franklin.

23Y • THE BOOK OF PHILADELPHIA. 1918. By Robert Shackleton.

24Y • THE LIFE & TIMES OF STEPHEN GIRARD, Vol. 1-2. 1918. By John Bach McMaster.

25Y • THE LITERARY HISTORY OF PHILADELPHIA. 1906. By E. P. Oberholtzer.

26Y • THE PICTURE OF PHILADELPHIA. 1811. By J. Mease, M.D.

27Y • THE RED CITY. 1908. By S. Weir Mitchell.

28Y • THE STRANGER'S GUIDE. 1811. By J. A. Paxton.

29Y • THOMAS'S HISTORY OF PHILADELPHIA AND WEST NEW JERSEY. 1698. By Gabriel Thomas.

30Y • WALKS AND TALKS ABOUT OLD PHILADELPHIA. 1928. By George Barton.

Drawn by Joseph Pennell, (1857-1926) famed author and etcher, this scene shows three story brick building at 119 South Front Street, Philadelphia, where North America opened for business on December 15th, 1792. Rear windows afforded view of spars and rigging along vessel-crowded Delaware River.

31Y • STEPHEN GIRARD'S WILL. 1831.

32Y • BIOGRAPHY OF A BUSINESS. 1942. By Marquis James. The Bobbs-Merrill Company.

33Y • HISTORY OF INSURANCE COMPANY OF NORTH AMERICA, 1792. By Thomas H. Montgomery, 1885.

34Y • LONELY MIDAS. 1943. By Harry Emerson Wildes. Farrar & Rinehart.

35Y • EPISODES OF HISTORY IN THE STORIES OF UNITED STATES AND THE INSURANCE COMPANY OF NORTH AMERICA, 1792-1917. 1916. Privately Printed.

In this charming, placid river scene of 1844, George Lehman, of Philadelphia, leaves us a document of historical significance and a painting of rare beauty. The covered bridge known as Gray's Ferry in Philadelphia crossed the Schuylkill at a point where most of the travelers on horse and in coaches arrived from the South. On an earlier pontoon bridge at Gray's Ferry, George Washington crossed in 1789 on his way to be inaugurated as President in New York. Note steam vessel at extreme left.

Vision of a Nation

*I*N addition to the documents and relics of bygone volunteer days, North America has preserved an unusual group of paintings and prints bearing upon the vast panorama of the nation's growth. In these views, the horizons of life range far and wide. The works of many American and European artists are represented in portraits, scenes, and landscapes painted over a stretch of years. One of the rarest paintings in this group is a portrait of Benjamin Franklin, by C. O. Wright in 1795, showing "Poor Richard" as a fireman.

Among the treasured "documentary paintings" are James Queen's "Rope Ferry Bridge" and Isaac Williams' "The Old Hotel." In these works, painted when photography had hardly emerged from Daguerre's studio, the charming and graceful scenes of a bygone day are recorded for posterity.

In the prints of historical interest, many distinguished American engravers and lithographers have left us scenes that depict the life of their times. Views of Philadelphia include rare engravings of the city, and a print of the first water-works in America, located on the site of the present City Hall. There is a splendid engraving of New York as it looked in 1834 from Governor's Island. A prospect of San Francisco in 1850 recalls the rush upon that city after the discovery of gold in California. In no other place on earth in so short a space of time has so much history taken place as in America during its rapid continental expansion in the last century. In no other part of the world has man covered the landscape so quickly with bridges, farms, oil wells, roads, skyscrapers, and homes.

In these recaptured glimpses of America, The North America's Collection summons up a broad view of days when the nation was hewing its destiny out of the raw material of a continent. Here are more than pictures: here is a whole vision of America building towns, bridges, farms, and railroads on a scale never before imagined in the history of mankind.

Here is inspiration from the past to light the days of our future. For here is the land we love.

PAINTINGS

1Z • ANDREW JACKSON AT BATTLE OF NEW ORLEANS, dated 1834. By Joseph Kyle.

2Z • BENJAMIN FRANKLIN, THE FIREMAN, dated 1795. By C. O. Wright.

3Z • BENJAMIN FRANKLIN, dated 1830. Thumb Portrait. By David R. Etter.

4Z • FORT LAFAYETTE, Narrows, New York City. 1868. Artist unknown.

5Z • FAIRMOUNT, near Philadelphia, dated 1842. By George Lehman. (*Illustrated*).

6Z • GYPSY CAMP. By Eastman Johnson.

7Z • GRAY'S FERRY, dated 1844. By George Lehman. (*Illustrated*).

8Z • INDEPENDENCE HALL. By W. H. Smith.

9Z • LANDSCAPE. By Harrington Fitzgerald.

10Z • LANDSCAPE. By William Sommer.

11Z • NIAGARA FALLS. By John McLure Hamilton.

12Z • PENROSE FERRY. Circa 1840. Rope Ferry Bridge over Schuylkill River. By James Queen. (*Illustrated*).

13Z • SIGNING OF DECLARATION OF INDEPENDENCE. By H. A. Ogden.

14Z • THE OLD HOTEL. Circa 1840, Manayunk. By Isaac Williams. (*Illustrated*).

15Z • WINTER SCENE. By Walter Schofield.

A charming pastel painting by James Queen, a Philadelphia artist, active in the middle 19th century. Queen has painted "from Nature" a view of Penrose Rope Ferry, named for Samuel Penrose, proprietor of the ferry across the Schuylkill River in 1776 at Philadelphia. Ferries were drawn across by ropes rigged from shore to shore. River navigators often cut ropes which ferrymen were supposed to keep submerged when not in use.

"Main Street Below Green Lane, Manayunk," by Isaac L. Williams, who studied art in Philadelphia with famed John Neagle. This scene, circa 1840, shows inn and stage coaches along Schuylkill River Canal at Philadelphia. Manayunk was Indian word for "Place-where-we-drink-water."

Rare and beautiful painting of Philadelphia on the Schuylkill River at Fairmount, dated 1842, by George Lehman. Group of buildings at far side of river comprises early water-works. Wire suspension bridge in distance was first large bridge of this type in the nation. Canal boats brought goods from upper reaches of the river in Pennsylvania; anthracite coal was carried in great quantities on this route.

New York City, circa 1834, is shown from Governor's Island in this fine engraving by John Hill, after a painting by W. G. Wall. At this time New York's maritime activity was being stimulated by the Erie Canal. Note "forest" of masts along water-front. Hill engraved many excellent scenes of American cities in this period. At right is Castle Williams, built in 1807.

PRINTS, ENGRAVINGS AND LITHOGRAPHS

16Z • ABRAHAM LINCOLN. Engraving. By Max Rosenthal.

17Z • CHARLESTON, Metropolis of Province of South Carolina. Engraved for London Magazine.

18Z • ENCAMPMENT OF THE AMERICAN ARMY AT VALLEY FORGE, 1788. Under command of General George Washington, Commander-in-chief.

19Z • ENGLISH STAGE COACH, 1847. Hand-woven silk print. By Thomas Stevens.

20Z • FALL OF RICHMOND. April 2, 1865. Lithograph. By Currier & Ives.

21Z • FAIRMOUNT WATER WORKS.

22Z • FIRST OFFICE OF INSURANCE COMPANY OF NORTH AMERICA. 119 S. Front Street, Phila. By Joseph Pennell.

23Z • GIRARD COLLEGE, 1848. From drawing by A. Kollner. By Deray.

24Z • INDEPENDENCE HALL, Philadelphia. By Gilbert.

25Z • JOHNSTOWN FLOOD, May 31, 1889.

26Z • MERCHANT'S EXCHANGE. From original drawing by A. Kollner. By Deray.

27Z • NEW YORK STOCK EXCHANGE. Engraving.

28Z • NEW YORK, 1834. From Governor's Island· Engraved by J. Hill. Painted by W. G. Wall. Issued circa 1835. Provenance: No. 20 Hudson River Portfolio. (*Illustrated*).

29Z • PHILADELPHIA, 1778. The Carwitham view, 2nd state. Published by Carington Bowles, London.

30Z • PHILADELPHIA. Upper Ferry Bridge.

31Z • PHILADELPHIA. From West Park. By Perkins.

32Z • PHILADELPHIA, 1850. From Camden.

33Z • PHILADELPHIA AND ENVIRONS. Engraving by J. Serz.

34Z • PHILADELPHIA, 1821. Print published in London.

35Z • PHILADELPHIA STATE HOUSE. Engraving.

36Z • PHILADELPHIA, 1863. French Engraving.

37Z • PHILADELPHIA. View of City. By C. O. Childs.

38Z • PHILADELPHIA. Water Front Scene. Lithograph.

39Z • PORTSMOUTH, N. H., 1837. Engraving.

40Z • PRESIDENT FILMORE'S RECEPTION, 1851. Navy Yard, Philadelphia.

41Z • PENNSYLVANIA HOSPITAL AND DEAF AND DUMB ASYLUM, 1854.

42Z • PEYTONA & FASHION, 1845. Horse Racing Scene. By Currier & Ives.

43Z • RAILROAD. Locomotive "Planet" 1834. Camden & Perth Amboy Railroad. By E. L. Henry.

44Z • SAN FRANCISCO. Engraving.

45Z • SCHUYLKILL RIVER DAM. Engraving.

46Z • STATE HOUSE, Philadelphia, Pa., 1752. Engraving.

47Z • VIEW OF FAIRMOUNT WATER WORKS, Philadelphia. By C. O. Childs.

48Z • WALL STREET, New York City.

49Z • WHITE'S PROCESSION OF VICTUALLERS. March 15, 1821. Lithograph. By Dubois. After painting by J. L Krimmel.

50Z • WATER WORKS ON SCHUYLKILL RIVER, Philadelphia. By Childs after Doughty.

51Z • WILLIAM PENN. Engraving. By J. Sartain. After H. Inman.

52Z • WOOD CUT PRINT. 115 Chestnut Street, Philadelphia, showing first fire mark plate of Insurance Company of North America. Print.

53Z • WOOD CUT PRINT. New York City.

54Z • WATER WORKS, Center Square, Philadelphia. Engraving. By C. Tiebout after J. J. Barralet.

THE HISTORICAL COLLECTION
IS NATIONALLY FAMOUS

IN many museums, libraries, universities and colleges throughout the United States, exhibits of The Historical Collection of the Insurance Company of North America are attracting more and more interest and attention. The material is a source for study and research among scholars because of its special historical value. Moreover, since it embraces the activities of those whose high deeds of valor and courage are written indelibly upon the chapters of American life, this historical material is interesting to all Americans.

The reason for the popularity of The Historical Collection lies in its ability to project out of the past those traditions which we, as Americans, hold in high esteem. A museum of history in a large city, having an exhibition relating to fire-fighting, recently wrote as follows: "Thousands of visitors are getting real pleasure out of the fire-fighting material from The Historical Collection of the Insurance Company of North America, which is now on view in this institution. We have observed that young and old of both sexes are absorbed by the many prints and objects that bring to life the stirring days of the bucket brigade and the hand-drawn pumpers. Just the other day, a businessmen's club spent more than an hour poring with delight over the exhibition. The Historical Collection of the Insurance Company of North America is performing a great service in affording the public an opportunity to enjoy these rare pieces. They are at once instructive and immensely interesting to the average person."

Exhibits from The Historical Collection of the Insurance Company of North America are in the following educational and cultural institutions:

ATWATER KENT MUSEUM	*Philadelphia, Penna.*
BUCKS COUNTY HISTORICAL SOCIETY	*Doylestown, Penna.*
BUFFALO HISTORICAL SOCIETY	*Buffalo, New York*
CATHOLIC UNIVERSITY OF AMERICA	*Washington, D. C.*
CHARTERED INSURANCE INSTITUTE	*London, England*
CHILDREN'S MUSEUM	*Indianapolis, Ind.*
CITY OF SAVANNAH	*Savannah, Georgia*
COLLEGE OF WILLIAM AND MARY	*Williamsburg, Va.*
CONFEDERATE MUSEUM	*Richmond, Va.*
CORNELL UNIVERSITY	*Ithaca, N. Y.*
DALLAS HISTORICAL SOCIETY	*Dallas, Texas*
DRUID HILL PARK MUSEUM	*Baltimore, Md.*
DUKE UNIVERSITY	*Durham, N. C.*
FORDHAM UNIVERSITY	*New York City, N. Y.*
FRANKLIN AND MARSHALL COLLEGE	*Lancaster, Pa.*
THE FRANKLIN INSTITUTE	*Philadelphia, Pa.*
HISTORICAL SOCIETY OF WESTERN PENNA.	*Pittsburgh, Pa.*
INDEPENDENCE HALL	*Philadelphia, Pa.*
KALAMAZOO MUSEUM AND ART INSTITUTE	*Kalamazoo, Michigan*
LOS ANGELES MUSEUM OF HISTORY, SCIENCE AND ART	*Los Angeles, Calif.*

LOUISIANA STATE MUSEUM	*New Orleans, La.*
MUSEUM OF THE CITY OF NEW YORK	*New York, N. Y.*
MUSEUM OF SCIENCE AND INDUSTRY	*Chicago, Ill.*
NEW YORK FIRE DEPT. MUSEUM	*New York, N. Y.*
OLD STATE HOUSE	*Boston, Massachusetts*
PENNSYLVANIA STATE COLLEGE	*State College, Pa.*
PENNSYLVANIA STATE MUSEUM	*Harrisburg, Pa.*
PRINCETON UNIVERSITY	*Princeton, N. J.*
SMITHSONIAN INSTITUTION, U. S. NATIONAL MUSEUM	*Washington, D. C.*
TOLEDO MUSEUM	*Toledo, Ohio*
UNITED STATES MILITARY ACADEMY	*West Point, N. Y.*
UNIVERSITY OF MICHIGAN	*Ann Arbor, Mich.*
UNIVERSITY OF VIRGINIA	*Charlottesville, Va.*
VALLEY FORGE MUSEUM	*Valley Forge, Pa.*
VANDERBILT MUSEUM	*Nashville, Tenn.*
VILLANOVA COLLEGE	*Villanova, Penna.*
VETERAN FIREMEN OF NEWBURGH	*Newburgh, Pa.*
WASHINGTON AND LEE UNIVERSITY	*Lexington, Va.*
WESTERN RESERVE HISTORICAL SOCIETY	*Cleveland, Ohio*
YALE UNIVERSITY	*New Haven, Conn.*

Exhibits from North America's Collection are to be seen in the Smithsonian Institution, Washington, D. C.
Photo from U. S. National Museum

The Franklin Institute, Philadelphia, is one of many museums in which material from The Collection is displayed.
Courtesy of The Franklin Institute

On Fifth Avenue, the Museum of the City of New York has a year 'round exhibition from North America's Collection.
Courtesy of Museum of City of New York

Thousands of visitors have seen items from The Collection at the Museum of Science and Industry at Chicago.
Courtesy of Museum of Science and Industry

At Independence Hall, the nation's shrine, part of The Collection is on permanent view.

The Collection is represented in California at the Los Angeles Museum of History, Science and Art.

Courtesy of Los Angeles Museum of History, Science and Art